NEW TECHNOLOGY
MADE EASY
for Seniors®

The User-Friendly Guidebook to Smartphones, Smart TVs, Super Sites, Computers, and More

(It Doesn't Have to be So Complicated!)

Publisher's Note

This book is intended for general information only. It does not constitute medical, legal, or financial advice or practice. The editors of FC&A have taken careful measures to ensure the accuracy and usefulness of the information in this book. While every attempt has been made to assure accuracy, errors may occur. Some websites, addresses, and telephone numbers may have changed since printing. We cannot guarantee the safety or effectiveness of any advice or treatments mentioned. Readers are urged to consult with their professional financial advisors, lawyers, and health care professionals before making any changes.

Any health information in this book is for information only and is not intended to be a medical guide for self-treatment. It does not constitute medical advice and should not be construed as such or used in place of your doctor's medical advice. Readers are urged to consult with their health care professionals before undertaking therapies suggested by the information in this book, keeping in mind that errors in the text may occur as in all publications and that new findings may supersede older information.

The publisher and editors disclaim all liability (including any injuries, damages, or losses) resulting from the use of the information in this book.

Have I not commanded you? Be strong and courageous. Do not be afraid; do not be discouraged, for the Lord your God will be with you wherever you go.

Joshua 1:9

FC&A Publishing®
103 Clover Green
Peachtree City, GA 30269
www.fca.com

Produced by the staff of FC&A

ISBN 978-1935574-93-4

Table of Contents

Desktops and Laptops

Tablets

Your Devices

Digital Security

Health and Fitness

Desktops and Laptops

1

A buyer's guide to computers

In the early days of consumer computing it was easy to buy a computer — you simply went to the store and bought one. However, what was undoubtedly a simpler time is now a long-distant memory. Consumers are faced with a seemingly endless choice of tech gadgets and decisions. Do you need a desktop or a laptop? Or would you be better off with a tablet? Is it powered with Windows or macOS? The options are overwhelming even for the most tech-savvy shoppers. With a little know-how you can cut through the jargon and find the best computer for your needs.

Pick the perfect computer with this expert advice

When you're shopping for a new computer it's easy to be drawn into thinking that you need to get the newest, most expensive one on the market. However, most people don't need all the latest bells and whistles. Instead, you should base your decision on one simple rule — buy a computer that does what you need it to do, rather than try to make use of all of its features. To achieve this, compile a list of what you want to do with your computer. This could include activities such as:

- Surf the web.

- Send emails.

- Video chat with family and friends.

- Perform everyday household productivity tasks.

- Stream movies and TV shows.

Once you have decided what you want from a computing device, you can then look for the best one in terms of power and functionality. If you order one online, you will be able to spend as much time as you like looking at the specifications of each device without a salesperson watching over you. Here are some things to consider when choosing a new machine.

Operating System (OS). This is essentially the program that brings your computer to life. It provides all of the functionality and enables you to interact with the computer. Without it, you would be staring at a blank screen. The main operating systems are Windows and macOS.

Processor. Also known as the CPU (Central Processing Unit), this is the part of a computing device that processes all of the instructions and commands from the operating system and apps. The speed of processors is usually measured in gigahertz (GHz) and the higher the number, the faster the processor. Look for a minimum of 2GHz.

Random Access Memory (RAM). This stores apps and data the computer is using, and is one of the most important indicators of how quickly it can operate. It is usually measured in gigabytes (GB). Look for a minimum of 8GB.

Hard Drive. This is the permanent memory, or storage, where data can be kept. For instance, the photos on your computer will be saved here. It is measured in gigabytes (GB), or even terabytes (TB). One TB equals 1,000 GB.

Ports and slots. Desktop computers and laptops have a range of ports and slots around the body of the device. These can be used to connect external devices, also known as peripherals. One of the most common is a USB slot, for connecting devices with a USB cable.

Removable storage. This includes devices such as external hard drives and flash drives, also known as thumb drives, that can be connected to a computer via a USB slot. Use these to back up or transfer files and folders.

Computer manufacturers release new, updated models regularly, often on an annual basis. One way to save money is to buy the previous year's model when the latest one is released. This will still provide you with a computer that will meet all of your needs while potentially providing you with significant savings.

Make sense of common software slang

When you're trying to navigate the tech world, you may stumble across a bewildering range of terms. If you don't know what they mean, you may find yourself hopelessly confused while you try to diagnose problems or learn new skills. These basic terms will help you talk tech like a pro.

App. This is just a more modern name for what used to be called a computer program.

Virus. This covers a wide range of malicious software programs that are used to disrupt your computing device or compromise your personal data. Sometimes called malware.

Cloud computing. This refers to the use of remote computers, known as servers, to back up, store, and manage folders and files from your tech devices.

6 tech tips that will make you a computer whiz

Using a computer need not be a daunting task. Here are a few simple but effective skills to get you started.

- Restart. Turn your computer off and back on again. It's the oldest tech trick in the book, but if your computer is not working as it should, it often helps to solve the problem.

- Undo. This is one of the simplest but most effective computer skills to learn. It reverses the previous action to quickly rectify mistakes. On your keyboard, press Ctrl+Z on a Windows computer or Cmd+Z on a Mac.

- Right-click. Use the right-hand button on your mouse to access menus for the item that has been clicked on.

- Take a shortcut. Those F keys at the top of the keyboard actually have useful functions. Depending on the device, they can be used for tasks such as changing the screen brightness, amending the volume, and accessing the music controls. On some keyboards they can also be used with the Fn key for even more options.

- Select text. Double-click on a single word to select it. Triple-click within a sentence to select the whole sentence. Quadruple-click within a paragraph to select the whole paragraph. Otherwise, click and hold with your mouse cursor and drag it over text to select it.

- Experiment. Don't be frightened to try different things on your computer. It is unlikely you will do any permanent damage and you can usually undo any action.

Master your machine with simple step-by-step instructions

Want to learn how to use your computer from the privacy of your own home? Start by visiting these three websites.

- Google (*google.com*). Got a specific tech question? If something has gone wrong, it is almost certain that someone else has had the same issue. A solution will be available in the search results.

- YouTube (*youtube.com*). For anyone looking to learn more about their computer, YouTube has thousands of useful videos. Type your issue into the search bar to find videos covering specific topics.

- LinkedIn Learning (*linkedin.com/learning*). This subscription website provides video learning courses covering topics including technology. You can try it free for one month.

Do you prefer more personal instruction? Check out these free resources and learn how to do everything on your computer. Look for classes at local colleges, use libraries as a gold mine of valuable reference material, and drop in to senior centers for advice on a range of computing and tech issues.

10 super ways to speed up a clunky PC

You wouldn't replace your TV every few years, so why would you replace your computer that often? The performance of most deteriorates over time, but you can keep yours running fast and glitch-free for 10 years or more by following these simple steps.

Defragmenting. Also called defragging, this reorganizes the data on your hard drive so that all of the pieces of a file are in the same location. This makes your device work more efficiently. Defragging can be done once a month to keep your computer running as fast as possible. On a Windows computer, use the Defragment and Optimize Drives app by accessing the *Start menu* and searching for it. On a Mac computer, specific apps for defragmenting can be downloaded from the App Store.

Clean up your computer. This can clear cobwebs from your computer's memory and help speed it up. On a Windows machine, use the Disk Cleanup app, select the required drive, and click on the OK button. The cleanup options will be displayed. Check the ones you want to remove and click on the OK button. On a Mac, apps used for defragmenting can also usually be used for cleanup tasks.

Empty the Recycle Bin. When you delete files, they aren't erased. They remain on your computer until you clear out your Recycle Bin. It's easy to forget about this, but your Trash can quickly become clogged with deleted files.

Remove unused apps. These can take up unnecessary space on your computer and slow it down.

Check for viruses. These dangerous programs can make your computer grind to a halt. Use the default anti-virus app installed on your device. If you don't have one already, you can download one. Trusted programs include Norton and McAfee.

Keep your software up to date. Older versions may cause your performance to slow down. In addition, you may need to reboot your computer in order to install these updates.

Use an external hard drive. This will free up some of your computer's resources and help to run the latest apps and operating systems.

Upgrade your hard drive. Solid state drives (SSDs) offer faster load times and require less energy than conventional hard drive disks (HDD).

Add more Random Access Memory (RAM). If your computer is running slowly, don't even think about buying a new one until you have tried this. RAM manages the operations being performed by a computer. If you don't have enough, it could be the reason your computer feels sluggish.

Consider a new processor. Think of this as the brain of your computer. If it is getting old, upgrading to a newer model may greatly improve a computer's speed and overall performance. However, your computer may not be compatible with all processors. Research your options carefully before buying one.

Upgrading certain computer parts can be tricky, and if you're not experienced, you may cause permanent damage. If you're in doubt about how to change out the components, take your machine to a computer store to have it done by a professional.

If an app is frozen, press these magic keys and — presto — your stubborn computer is well-behaved once again.

- On a Windows computer press Ctrl+Alt+Delete, and click on the Task Manager option. This displays all currently open apps. If an app has a *Not responding* message next to it, click on the *End task* button. If in doubt, do this for all open apps that you think may be causing a problem.

- On a Mac, select the Apple icon from your top menu then Force Quit. Click on an app to select it and click on the *Force Quit* button to close it.

2 Windows 11

Windows is one of the most established operating systems for desktop computers and laptops. Experts estimate 3 out of every 4 computers run on some version of Windows. It has had numerous versions since it was first introduced in 1985. When Windows 10 was unveiled in 2015, Microsoft said there wouldn't be any new updates. However, nothing in the world of technology stands still for very long. In 2021, Microsoft changed their tune. They released the all-new Windows 11 with a fresh design and new features.

Microsoft regularly puts out updates for Windows. Depending on which version you are using, certain buttons and icons may appear slightly different than the ones described in this chapter.

2 top tips get you started with Windows 11

Want to update your Windows computer to the latest operating system? Simply go to the Settings icon on your Taskbar and select *Windows Update*. If Windows 11 is available it will be displayed here. Click on *Update Now* to get started.

After you finish installing the update, there are a couple more things you need to do before you can use your computer.

Set up this free account. A Microsoft account can help you organize digital files, stay up to date on privacy and security options for your computer, and sync settings across multiple devices. You can create an account during the initial setup of Windows 11. All you need is a username — like an email address — and a password.

Learn how to navigate the new Windows 11 Desktop. This is the first screen you see when you log on to Windows, so you need to know what everything is. Check out the main elements of the Desktop.

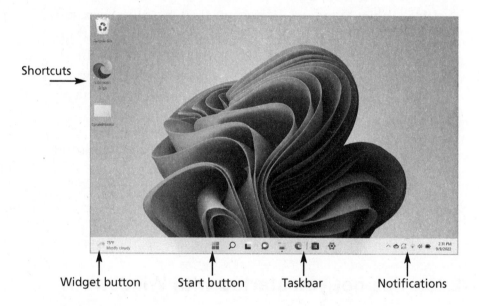

Shortcuts

Widget button   Start button   Taskbar   Notifications

Personalize your PC like a pro

Your computer and apps may not be set up exactly how you want. With a little know-how, you can customize them. All you have to do is go to Windows 11 Settings.

1. Click on the Settings icon in your Taskbar.

2. The main categories are listed in the left sidebar. Select a category to view items within it.

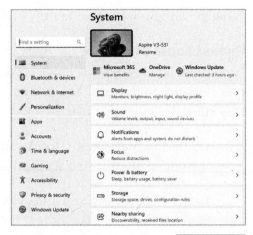

3. Select an item to view the customization options. Some may have buttons next to them. You can change these by dragging the button between *On* and *Off*.

If you want to go back to your previous page, click on the left-facing arrow in the top left corner of the Settings window.

Discover the all-new Start menu

The Start menu provides access to all of your apps and important areas of your computer. To get to it, click on the Start icon on the left-hand side of the Taskbar.

Want to customize how the Start menu looks? Follow these steps.

1. Click on the Settings icon, which by default will appear as pinned in your Start menu.

2. Click on *Personalization* in the left-hand sidebar.

3. Click on *Start*.

4. Select a layout for the Start menu.

5. Choose which items to display on the Start menu.

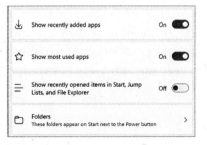

Now get to know specific features of the Start menu.

Pinned apps. The top of the Start menu displays apps that have been pinned, or saved, for quick access. They will remain here unless you change them. You can edit these apps by following these easy steps.

1. Using the Start menu, locate any app which you want to include in the Pinned section.

2. Right-click on the app and select the *Pin to Start* option.

3. To remove an app from the Pinned section, right-click on it and click on the *Unpin from Start* option. Apps removed from the Pinned section are not deleted from your computer.

   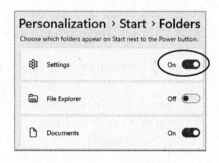

Recently opened files. The bottom portion of the Start menu shows pictures, documents, and other files that you have just used. Click on an icon to open it.

Quick access icons. The bottom toolbar of the Start menu offers shortcuts to frequently used areas on your computer, such as Settings or File Explorer. You can customize these items by going to Settings > Personalization > Start > Folders. Use the buttons to toggle items on this toolbar *On* or *Off*.

Personalization › Start › Folders
Choose which folders appear on Start next to the Power button.

⚙ Settings — On
🗀 File Explorer — Off
🗋 Documents — On

All apps list. Want to use an app that isn't displayed under your favorites or on your Desktop? You can use the Start menu to view every app on your computer.

1. Click on the Start icon to display the Start menu and click on *All apps*.

2. The All apps list is displayed.

3. You can also move your cursor to the right-hand edge of the panel to view the scroll bar. Drag it up and down to view all the apps on your computer.

4. Click on a letter heading to display a panel that will allow you to jump to a different letter heading.

5. Return to the Start menu at any time by selecting the *Back* button.

Master the Taskbar to keep everything at your fingertips

The Taskbar is a row of icons located along the bottom of your Desktop. If you know how to use it properly, this tool makes it easy to quickly access the apps and files you need most often.

Find all your open windows. If you're using an app that could have several different windows running at once, the Taskbar makes it a snap to keep track of them. Here's how to check what you have open.

1. Move your cursor over any app icon on the Taskbar.

2. If an app has open windows, they will be displayed as thumb-nails, or small versions of the window, above the Taskbar.

3. Click on one of the thumbnails to expand it and bring it to the front of your Desktop.

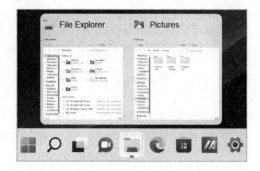

Pin apps to the Taskbar. You can save all your favorite apps here for quick access.

1. Click on the Start button and go to any app.

2. Right-click on the app and select *Pin to taskbar*.

3. The selected app is added to the right-hand side of your Taskbar.

You can take apps off of your Taskbar by right-clicking on the app's icon, and selecting *Unpin from taskbar*.

Customize your Taskbar. Reposition apps by clicking and holding on them with your mouse cursor. Drag them to a new position on the Taskbar.

In the past, app icons were aligned to the left on the Taskbar at the bottom of the screen. Windows 11 adjusted it so that these icons are centered instead. If you're more comfortable with the older operating system, you can change this.

1. Click on the Settings app.

2. Click on *Personalization* in the left-hand sidebar.

3. Select the *Taskbar* option.

4. Scroll down the window and click on the *Taskbar behaviors* option.

5. Click the box next to *Taskbar alignment*.

6. Select *Left* to position the Start button and apps to the lower, left-hand corner.

Every time you start an app, it opens a new window on your Desktop. The one you currently have selected is known as your active window. If you have multiple apps open, you can switch between them by simply clicking the one you want to use.

To move windows around on your screen, click and hold the title bar located at the top of the window. Use your mouse to drag the window around your Desktop.

To quickly move between all of your open windows, press Alt+Tab. A panel displaying every open app, known as the Task Switcher, will open on your screen. Continue holding down the Alt key and press Tab to switch between windows. The selected app will have a thin border around it. Release both keys to bring it to the front of your screen.

4 secrets to a clutter-free screen

If you have too many windows open on your Desktop, your computer can quickly get bogged down with clutter. Here's how to keep everything organized and running smoothly.

Exit a single window. You can close out of a single window by clicking on the cross button in the top, right-hand, corner.

Minimize windows. To hide a window, click on this button in the top, right-hand corner. Your window will shrink off of the screen, but the app will continue to run in the background. To view it again, move your mouse cursor over the app's icon on the Taskbar. Click on the thumbnail displayed above the app's icon.

Maximize windows. If you want your window to take up your entire screen, click on this button in the top, right-hand corner. When you're ready to shrink it back to its original size, move the mouse cursor to the top of the screen. The control panel will reappear. Press this button to resize the window.

Close multiple windows. Using an app that has more than one window open? You can close them all at once by right-clicking on the app's icon on the Taskbar. Scroll down and select *Close all windows.*

Set a fast path to important files

File Explorer, which you use to manage all your folders and files, has a brand new look in Windows 11. You can find it in the Taskbar or the Start menu by selecting this icon.

It opens to a navigation panel which shows the main locations on your computer, such as *Desktop, Documents,* and *Pictures.* It also contains the *Home* folder, which stores shortcuts to frequently used folders and files. Here's how to add items to your *Home* folder.

- To add any folder to the Quick Access section, right-click on it and choose the *Pin to Quick Access* option.

- To add any file to the Favorites section, right-click on it and select *Pin to Favorites.*

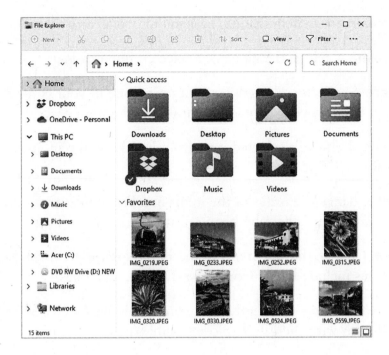

Become a menu expert with this handy guide

In Windows 11 the File Explorer menu bar is a set of icons that appears along the top of the File Explorer window. These are, from left to right:

New. Create a new folder in File Explorer or open a selection of apps.

Cut. Remove an item but temporarily save it onto your clipboard.

Copy. Duplicate an item to your clipboard without removing it from its current location.

Paste. Insert an item that has been cut or copied into a new location.

Rename. Change the name of a selected file or folder.

Share. Share the selected item with someone in your contacts list. You can access your contacts from the Mail app.

Delete. Remove a selected item from File Explorer and place it in the Recycle Bin.

Sort. Change the order of the items in a File Explorer window. You can arrange them by Name, Date Modified, or Type.

View. Change the way items in the File Explorer are displayed. Options include Large Icons, List, Details, and Tiles.

Two of the most frequently used commands are Copy and Paste. To do this with the File Explorer menu bar:

1. Select an item, or items, in File Explorer.

2. Click on the *Copy* icon in the menu bar.

3. Use the locations on the left hand navigation bar to move within File Explorer. When you reach your desired location, click on the *Paste* icon on the menu bar.

You can also right-click on items or text and select *Copy* or *Paste* from the pop-up menu.

Stay up to date with the new Widgets panel

Widgets are small windows that display content from your favorite apps and websites. They can keep you updated on current topics like the news, sports scores, or the weather. Your computer has a

few default widgets. To
view them, click on the
live weather icon in the
far left corner of your
Taskbar. This will open a
panel that displays your
current widgets.

Customize your Widget panel. Want to keep your favorite widgets
at your fingertips? Add them to this panel with two easy steps.

1. Click on the account button located in the top, right-hand
    corner of the Widgets panel to view your settings.

2. A list of available widgets
    will appear under the Add
    Widgets section. Items
    already on your panel will
    have a ✓ symbol next to
    them. Click on the + sym-
    bol to add a new one.

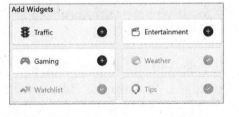

Click on the three dots in the top, right-hand corner of any widget
to view its settings. You can change its size or what information is
displayed. To change the location of a widget on your panel, click
the widget header and drag it to a new spot.

Personalize your Feed. The Widget panel displays a stream of
news items and widgets known as your Feed. You can tweak this
Feed to display content that most interests you.

1. Open the Widgets settings by selecting the account button in
    the top, right-hand corner of the panel.

2. Scroll down to the *Personalize your interests* button at the bottom of the Widgets settings page. Click on it.

3. This will open your web browser and take you to an internet page called My Interests.

4. The left-hand panel contains a list of categories. Click on one to see more options and topics under each category. The right-hand panel contains a search box and a list of the most common interests.

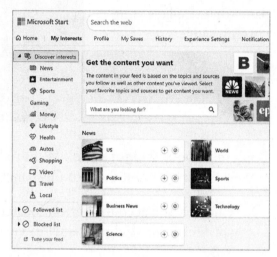

5. If you are curious about a topic, click on the + symbol next it. Your Feed will start to show content related to that topic.

To view all the subjects you are currently following and make changes, click on the *Followed list* option in the left-hand panel.

3 apps keep you connected

Your computer is great for keeping in touch with family and friends. Find these apps in the Taskbar or on the Start menu, and use them to stay connected.

Edge browser. This is the default web browser for Windows 11. Use this app to connect to the internet and view websites. However, you can download other browsers such as Firefox or Chrome.

Mail app. This is the default email program for Windows 11. Add your email account by clicking on the *Accounts* button in the left-hand sidebar. Enter your login details for the account you wish to add.

Chat app. Use this to send texts and video chats. A Microsoft account is required.

Tune out distractions with a brand-new feature

Most apps use notifications to alert you to updates, messages, or other new information. While these can be useful by making sure you don't miss out on anything important, they can quickly become overwhelming. If you're trying to concentrate on something else, you can mute notifications for a short period of time with Focus.

1. Open the Settings app and click on *System*.

2. Click on *Focus*.

3. Click the down-pointing arrow to the right of *Start focus session* to show the Focus options and to specify how long your notifications will be muted.

4. Click on the – and + buttons to set the duration of your Focus session.

5. Use the check boxes next to the options to toggle them on or off.

6. Click on the *Start focus session* button.

Split screen is now a Snap

When using your computer, you may want to see several files or web pages simultaneously. Windows 11 has a new feature called Snap that makes viewing multiple things at once a — well — snap. Here's how to use it.

1. Open any app and move your cursor over the square button in the top, right-hand corner of the window.

2. This displays the Snap layout panel.

3. Select one of the thumbnails from the panel. Your original app will now display using this chosen screen layout.

Depending on the layout you select, you may have the option to display additional apps on your Desktop. Click on an app in one of the layout windows to add it to the screen.

Want your PC to last? Follow these simple steps

Your computer needs regular maintenance to ensure that it stays in good working order for as long as possible. Windows 11 has several tools you can use to keep your operating system in top shape. Here's how to access them.

1. Open File Explorer and click on *This PC* in the left-hand navigation panel.

2. Right-click on the drive labeled (C:) then click on *Properties*.

3. Click on the *Tools* tab at the top of the *Properties* window to access the maintenance tasks. Use the *Check button* to look for any errors on the hard drive. Click on *Optimize* to analyze your drive to see if it needs to be defragmented.

The Settings app also has a troubleshoot function you can use to identify and repair issues with your computer. Go to Settings > System > Troubleshoot to access this tool.

Computer security may not be exciting, but it's critical you stay on top of it. Otherwise, you could hand sensitive personal information over to hackers. Here's how to make sure your data is safe and secure.

1. Go to the Settings app and click on *Privacy & security* in the left-hand sidebar.

2. The privacy and security options are shown in the main window.

3. Select *Windows Security*.

4. Click on the *Open Windows Security* button.

Use this tool to check for viruses, activate the built-in Windows Firewall, and run a general health check on your computer.

Easy reset dodges disaster

Don't panic if your computer is running slowly or freezing and you have no idea what the problem is. You can get it working again in no time by using System Restore. This will reset your computer to an earlier point in time when it was hopefully behaving properly. Follow these steps to perform a System Restore.

1. Open the Settings app and select System > About.

2. Select the *System Protection* tab.

3. Click on the *System Restore* button.

4. Press *Next*.

5. Choose a date and time in the System Restore menu when your computer was working properly. Click on the *Next* button.

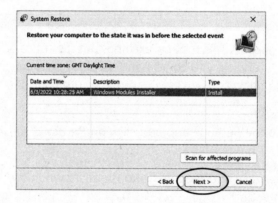

6. Confirm the restore point and press *Finish*.

Of course you must first have a restore point available for just such an emergency. In fact, it's a good idea to create new restore points regularly when your computer is running well.

To create one, go to Settings > System > About > Advanced System Settings. In the System Properties window, go to the System Protection tab and press *Create*. Choose a name for the restore point and click on the *Create* button.

Simply pressing the power button when you're ready to turn off your computer may be easy, but it can cause files to corrupt. Instead, make sure to properly shut down when you're finished. Here's how.

1. Right-click on the Start button and select *Shut down or sign out*. You can also press this icon in the Start menu.

2. Select *Shut down*.

Add new apps in a flash

Use the Microsoft Store to find and download new apps for your computer. To access it, click on this icon in the Taskbar or Start menu.

To find new apps, click on the category buttons in the left-hand sidebar. You can also use the Search box at the top of the window to type in keywords or app names.

Once you find an app you want, click on it to view the details. Press the *Get* button to download.

14 essential Windows keyboard tricks

Don't go to a menu every time you need to do a common task on your computer. Learn these shortcuts to save yourself tons of time.

Ctrl+S	Save a document
Ctrl+C	Copy a selected item
Ctrl+X	Cut a selected item
Ctrl+V	Paste an item that has been cut or copied
Ctrl+Z	Undo the previous action
Ctrl+W	Close the active window

These shortcuts use the WinKey on your keyboard to help you navigate menus, settings, and other Windows specific features.

⊞	Access the Start menu
⊞ +L	Lock the computer and display the Lock screen
⊞ +I	Access the Settings app
⊞ +Q	Access the Search window
⊞ +D	Access the Desktop
⊞ +E	Access File Explorer
⊞ +U	Access the Accessibility options in the Settings app
⊞ +T	Display the thumbnails of open items on the Taskbar

3 macOS Ventura

Apple's range of desktop and laptop computers, which includes iMacs, MacBooks, and the Mac mini, all use the company's proprietary operating system macOS. Currently, each new version is named after a famous place in California, the home state of Apple's headquarters. The newest version, macOS Ventura, is named after the coastal city in Southern California. It is designed to make Apple computers more compatible with mobile devices like iPads and iPhones.

Remember, menu names and icons may not be identical across different macOS operating systems. Depending on which version you use, certain buttons or apps may appear different.

3 features every Mac user needs to know

Any time you use a new operating system, you want to make sure you know the basics. The Desktop is the first thing you'll see after logging on to a Mac. Here are a few tips for navigating this screen.

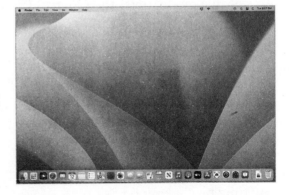

Work with one or more apps. When you open an app, it appears in a new window on your Desktop. Opening new apps will create more windows in front of your current one. Click on any open window to cycle it to the front.

You can also move windows around the screen by clicking and holding the top bar of the window and dragging it to a new position.

Juggle multiple windows with Stage Manager. This new feature can help you organize your screen while you are working with several apps at once. Here's how to use it.

1. Click this icon in the top, right-hand corner of the Desktop to open the Control Center.

2. Click on the *Stage Manager* button.

3. The window you're currently using moves to the center of the screen. Any other open windows appear on the sidebar at the left-hand side of your Desktop.

4. Click one of the windows in the sidebar to take it to the center of the screen. Your current window will move to the sidebar.

5. Click in any empty area on your Desktop to send all your open apps to the sidebar.

To exit this mode, open the Control Center again and select the *Stage Manager* button.

Navigate quickly with menus. Use menu bars to access options and functions for different apps. Find these at the top of your Desktop or in the top bar of some app windows. Click on a menu name to view more information.

Access the main computer menu, or the Apple menu, at any time by clicking on the apple icon in the top, left-hand corner of your screen.

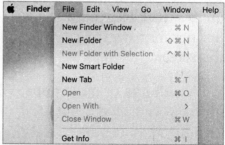

6 expert tips maximize Dock control

The Dock — a row of icons on the bottom of your Desktop — is one of the most important organizational tools on your Mac. It's divided into two sections. All your saved apps go on the left side of the dock. Minimized windows, the Trash icon, and other apps go on the right. Here are a few strategies for using your Dock efficiently.

- Click once on an app's icon in your Dock to open it. Open apps have a small dot displayed below their icon.

- Click and hold on an open app's icon. A menu displaying a list of open windows and available actions will pop up.

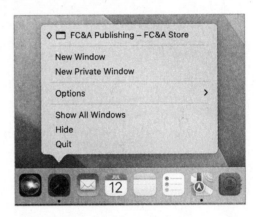

- To close an app from the Dock, click and hold on its icon. Select *Quit* from the pop-up menu.

- To adjust the size of icons, change the Dock's location on your Desktop, or to access other Dock settings, click on the System Settings icon on the Dock. Select the *Desktop & Dock* option.

- To add an app to your Dock, click on this icon to open the Finder. Open your Applications folder. Click and hold on any app and drag it onto your Dock.

- To remove an app from the Dock, click and hold on its icon. Drag it onto the Desktop until you see *Remove*. Release your mouse.

Handy tool finds anything in a flash

Use the Finder to locate all of your Mac's apps, documents, photos, and external devices. To access it, click on this icon in the Dock.

The left-hand panel is the Finder sidebar, which houses shortcuts to frequently used folders and locations on your computer. You can click on any item in the sidebar to view it in the main window. Here are a few more tips for using the Finder.

- Click and hold any item in your main Finder window. Drag it into the sidebar to create a shortcut.

- Click on this icon at the top of the Finder window to view display options for the main window.

- Click on this icon to organize and sort the items in your main window.

- Click on a folder or file in the Finder to select it. Then press this icon to view menu options for the selected item.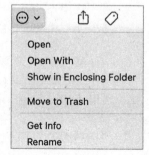

System Settings: New, fast, and friendly

In the past, Mac computers used an app called System Preferences to change settings and other options. However, Apple changed it up with macOS Ventura. They renamed it System Settings and redesigned the interface so that it feels similar to the ones on iPads and iPhones. Here's how to access this feature.

1. Click this icon in the Dock.

2. Select an item from the left-hand sidebar to view more options in the main window.

3. Scroll up and down the main window to view the full range of settings.

Take control with this fresh feature

People familiar with Apple's phones and tablets may already be acquainted with the Control Center. This panel — a staple on these devices for several years — can manage frequently used functions and settings. And now it's available on Mac computers, too. To access the Control Center, go to the top toolbar and click on this button.

Here are a few ways you can use the Control Center.

- Set options for Focus, which will temporarily turn off notifications.

- Turn on and manage Screen Mirroring, which can display your Mac's screen on another device.

- Turn Wi-Fi and Bluetooth on or off.

- Use AirDrop, which allows you to share items with nearby Apple devices.

- Alter the screen brightness and volume on your computer.

- Play and control tracks in the Music app.

Customize the options in your Control Center by going to System Settings > Control Center.

Don't let notifications overwhelm your Mac

Notifications are a common feature on most computers. These pop-ups alert you to new information, like the arrival of an email. In macOS Ventura, alerts appear in the Notification Center in the top right-hand corner of your Desktop. However, you may not want all your apps to send you alerts. To customize what you see, follow these steps.

1. Open System Settings and click on *Notifications* in the left-hand sidebar.

2. Items that will appear in the Notification Center are listed in the main window. Click on an item to select it and view its options. You can change the alert style, which deter-

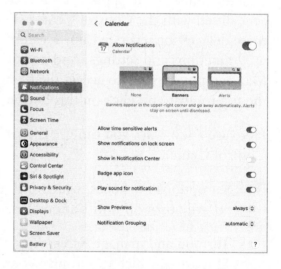

mines how Notifications will be displayed. Banner notifications show up on the screen for a few seconds. Alert notifications stay on your screen until you dismiss them.

3. To prevent an item from appearing in the Notification Center, click on it to select it. Set the *Allow Notifications* button to the left or off position.

To view all of your computer's notifications, click on the date and time in the top right-hand corner of the screen. A panel will appear with a list of all your notifications at the top. You can hide the panel by clicking on the date and time again.

Switch off distractions with the push of a button

Notifications can be a great way to keep on top of everything that is happening with your computer. But they can be a distraction if you are trying to concentrate on something else. The good news? You can use Focus to temporarily turn off alerts.

Limit interruptions with Do Not Disturb. Use this setting to mute all notifications for a short period of time. To turn it on, go to System Settings > Focus. Click on the *Do Not Disturb* option in the main window.

From this menu, you can specify how long you want to mute your notifications and customize which apps can still send you notifications. If you have a specific time during the day that you like to work without interruption, simply schedule a Do Not Disturb session. Click the *Turn On Automatically* button to set one up.

Create your own Focus modes. You may want to turn off notifications from certain apps or contacts during different times of the day. So create your own custom focus mode.

1. Go to System Settings > Focus. Click on *Do Not Disturb*.

2. Choose one of the Focus modes in the main window. You can select from the displayed list or click the *Add Focus...* button to view more options.

3. Click on *Allowed People* to select who can contact you while your Focus mode is active.

4. Click on the *Add* button to select contacts who can still send you notifications.

5. Click the *Done* button when you are finished to go back to the main menu.

6. From here, click on the *Allowed Apps* option and use the *Add* button to choose apps that can still create alerts during your custom Focus mode.

Get wise to widgets in 6 easy steps

Widgets are a bit like mini apps for your computer. They give you a quick glance at information from your favorite websites or apps.

You can use them to check the weather, sports scores, or even stock prices. Here's how to customize and view your widgets in macOS Ventura.

1. Click on the date and time in the upper right-hand corner of the Desktop to open the Notifications Center. This panel will display your notifications at the top and your widgets below.

2. Click on the *Edit Widgets* button at the bottom of this panel.

3. A new window will open. Widgets already in your Notification Center are shown in the right-hand panel.

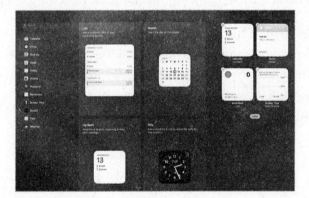

4. All of the available widgets are shown in the left-hand panel. Click on one to see a preview and view details about it in the middle panel.

5. Some widgets may have *S, M,* or *L* buttons below them in the middle panel. Select one to choose the widget's size.

6. Click on a widget in the middle panel to add it to your Notification Center. You can also move your cursor over the widget and click on the + button to add it.

Don't miss this: 2 top ways to navigate your Mac

Want to quickly access your favorite apps and documents? These two features ensure that everything you need is only a click away.

Launchpad. This function displays all of the apps on your Mac. To open it, press F4 on your keyboard or click on this icon on the Dock.

You'll see a new window displaying all your apps. Click on any one to open it. If you have multiple pages of apps, you can click on the dots at the bottom of the screen to cycle through them. Any new apps you download will show up on the final page of the Launchpad.

Mission Control. This feature lets you view all currently open windows and apps on your Mac. Press F3 on your keyboard or select this icon in your Dock to view all your open windows. Click on any window to bring it to the front of your Desktop.

Made a mistake? Take back that text

Oops. You just sent an instant text message only to realize it was addressed to the wrong person. Or maybe you noticed a typo too late. In the past, there wasn't much you could do. Now, macOS has a new feature that will allow you to edit and unsend certain text messages. Here's how.

1. While pressing Ctrl on your keyboard, use your mouse to click on a message in the Messages app.

2. Click on either the *Undo Send* or *Edit* option. These will be available for up to 15 minutes after sending the message but only on any thread that is using iMessage — not SMS text messages.

3. Messages that have been unsent will be immediately removed.

4. If you choose *Edit*, change the text and then click on the blue check mark to the right of the text box.

Using the Mail app, you can also unsend an email for up to 10 seconds after it has been sent, but you can't edit it.

Note this new feature only works if you are communicating with somebody who is also using macOS Ventura. If they are on a different operating system or running an earlier version of macOS, they may still see the original message.

Passwords are vital for keeping your information safe — but it can be tough to remember them all. Mac's default web browser, Safari, has a new feature called Passkeys that can help you stay secure without needing to remember dozens of different passwords.

Whenever you create a new online account on a website, you can now create a Passkey that will let you log in again. These are stored on your computer and synchronized across other Apple devices, such as iPads and iPhones.

Wrap it up: 3 options for logging off

When you're finished using your Mac, you have a few choices. Simply click on the Apple Menu and select from *Sleep*, *Restart*, or *Shut Down*. Here's what each one does.

- Select *Sleep* to put your Mac into a power-saving mode. Your computer will remain turned on, but it uses less electricity.

- Select *Restart* to turn your computer off and immediately back on.

- Select *Shut Down* to turn your computer completely off.

When you choose *Restart* or *Shut Down*, a box will pop up and ask if you wish to confirm or cancel. If you do nothing, the process will start after 60 seconds. If you want the windows and apps you are using to start back up when you turn on your computer again, check the box that says *Reopen windows when logging back in*.

Always make sure to save any work on your computer before shutting down or restarting. Although your computer will prompt you to go back and save before it turns off, it's a good habit to have.

Keep your computer secure with this 1 feature

You must stay on top of security settings to protect your computer and your information. To access these on a Mac, go to System Settings > Security & Privacy.

- General. Set up a password for your Mac's login screen.

- FileVault. Encrypt the data on your Mac.

- Firewall. Set up the Mac's built-in firewall, which can stop viruses from invading your computer.

- Privacy. Determine which apps can access your location data, your built-in camera, your microphone, and your files.

11 brilliant Mac keyboard shortcuts

Keystroke shortcuts can save you tons of time when you're using your computer. To perform common tasks, you'll press and hold two or three keys at once on your Mac keyboard. They all include the Command (cmd) ⌘ key.

⌘+A	Select all items in your current window
⌘+C	Copy a selected item
⌘+H	Hide your current window
⌘+M	Minimize your current window
⌘+N	Open a new window for the app you are using
⌘+S	Save the document you are currently using
⌘+T	Open a new tab
⌘+V	Paste an item that has been copied
⌘+W	Close your current window
⌘+Z	Undo the previous action
⌘+Shift+H	Open the Home folder in Finder

Top 10 Tips for
Desktops and Laptops

1. Purchase the best desktop or laptop by first evaluating your own needs. Consider what features you'll actually use instead of opting for the fastest, newest models.

2. Take some time to learn terms used in the tech world. It can help when you're choosing a device.

3. If one of your devices is having trouble, turn it off and on again. You may be surprised by the results.

4. Cycle through apps in Windows 11 by using the Task Switcher. Hold down Alt on your keyboard and tap the Tab key to move between apps.

5. The Windows 11 File Explorer has a set of menu buttons at the top of each window. Use them to perform common tasks such as Copy, Paste, Rename, and Delete.

6. The Windows 11 Widgets are an excellent way to keep up to date on topics such as news, sports, entertainment, and travel.

7. Use the Chat app in Windows 11 to send text messages or make video calls.

8. Mac users need to know that macOS Ventura renamed System Preferences to System Settings.

9. Use the Stage Manager in macOS Ventura to focus on one main window while still being able to view your other open apps.

10. The Control Center in macOS Ventura gives you quick access to frequently used options and settings, such as Wi-Fi, screen brightness, and volume controls.

Tablets

4

The ABC's of tablets

Tablets are a happy medium between computers and smartphones. They're smaller, lighter, and more portable than laptops, but they offer larger screens and bigger batteries than phones. That makes them great for reading e-books, working on the go, or watching movies and videos. If you decide you want to get a tablet, you don't necessarily need to buy the latest, high-end model. First decide what you'll use it for. Will you spend most of your time surfing the web and sending emails? Or maybe you want a bigger screen for those family video chats. Once you know what you want, you can start hunting for the best tablet without breaking the bank.

Make tablet shopping a breeze

Ready to get a tablet? You have dozens of choices — which may seem overwhelming at first. But if you know where to look, you can research products and compare prices from the comfort of your own home.

Pick the best tech in a snap. If you don't know much about electronics, but you need to buy a new tablet, phone, laptop, TV, camera, or printer, don't worry. No need to spend hours slogging through reviews. These unbiased websites offer expert advice on choosing the best tech.

- *Nytimes.com/wirecutter*
- *Cnet.com*
- *PCmag.com*

You'll love how much money you can save with these easy-to-use websites. After you've chosen the tablet you want to buy, the next step is hunting down the best price. The fastest, easiest way to do that? Use these instant price comparison websites to locate the best deals while you shop.

- *Shopsavvy.com*

- *Pricegrabber.com*

- *Shopping.com*

- *Shopzilla.com*

If you order tech gadgets online, always check the delivery costs. These fees can significantly push up the price of an item. You may end up overpaying for something even though you think you're getting a deal.

7 must-know tech terms

When you're in the market for a new tablet, you may stumble across words that make your head spin. But don't worry. This handy guide can help you understand confusing tech jargon.

Processor or chip. Think of this a bit like the brain of a tablet. It determines how quickly the device can operate and perform tasks. The speed of this part is usually measured in gigahertz (GHz).

Storage. This determines how much content — such as pictures and apps — your tablet can store. It is usually measured in gigabytes (GB) or terabytes (TB).

Connectivity. Tablets have different options for connecting to the internet. Some may use only Wi-Fi, while others can use cell signal like 5G. Some tablets also have Bluetooth, which can be used to connect with nearby computers, phones, and accessories.

Cameras. Most tablets have two cameras. One on the front that is used for video calling and selfies, and another on the back for higher quality photos and videos.

Operating system. This is the main software that powers a tablet. You may want to consider which one you'll use based on how well it synchronizes with your other tech devices. For example, if you use Apple computers and phones, you may want to opt for an Apple tablet. Or if you have an Android phone, you may prefer an Android tablet.

Battery power. This determines how long a tablet can run on a single charge. Look for a model that offers at least 10 hours per charge for general use, such as surfing the web or listening to music. However, you should know that certain apps or settings may cause the battery to drain faster.

Input and Output options. Consider what kind of cables can connect to the tablet. This can limit the type of accessories you use.

Master the basics with this handy guide

Sometimes even turning on your tablet can be confusing. So here's what you do. Search around the edge of the device for the power button. Once you find it, press and hold it until the screen lights up or your device plays a sound. Once it's up and running, you'll need to know these basics, too.

Home screen. This is the first screen you see when you turn on your tablet. It displays some or all of the apps on the tablet.

Home button. You can press this button to return to the Home screen at any time. Depending on your tablet, this may be a physical button or an icon.

Apps. These are the programs on your tablet. Open them by tapping on the app's icon.

Dock or Favorites Tray. This is the bar at the bottom of an iPad or an Android tablet, where shortcuts to your most frequently used apps can be kept for easy access.

Settings. Access options for customizing your tablet by tapping on the standard gear icon.

Navigate your tablet with 5 essential gestures

Unlike traditional computers, you won't use a mouse and keyboard to get around your tablet. Instead, you'll navigate the touch screen with your fingers. Here are some of the most common swipes, taps, and presses.

- Swipe to swap between Home screens. Some tablets may have multiple Home screens which are used to display the apps on your device. To cycle through them, drag your finger to swipe left or right on the Home screen.

- Double tap on a web page or photo to zoom in. Repeat the process to go back to your original view.

- Place your thumb and forefinger close together on the screen and slowly slide them apart to zoom in on documents, photos, or web pages. Move them back together to zoom out.

- Press and hold on an app's icon to view available menu options.

- Move apps around your Home screen by pressing and holding on the app's icon and dragging it to a new position. Release your finger to lock it in that new spot on the screen.

2 super strategies help your tablet last for years

If you want your tablet to remain in good condition for as long as possible, you need to protect it. These two accessories are a great way to make sure your device stands the test of time.

Covers and cases. These fit over the body of your tablet and give it protection from scrapes and bumps. Some covers even absorb the shock from drops and falls. You can buy covers that go over the screen when it is not in use, which helps protect the fragile glass.

Screen protectors. These are clear plastic or glass covers that fit directly on top of your tablet's screen. They help protect the touch screen from scratches, cracks, and other damage.

Tablets are valuable tools to have in the kitchen. They're great for looking up recipes and watching videos that take you through step-by-step cooking instructions. But be careful. Splashes and splatters make the kitchen a precarious place for your tablet. Make sure to keep it away from water and other liquids. One bright idea — cover the screen with plastic wrap while you're cooking.

Spend cash on add-ons you're sure to use

Accessories for your tablet can be necessary, cool, or just plain fun. While there's no need to buy every single add-on you can find, consider whether or not these will make your computing experience better.

Stands. These prop up your tablet so you can use it without holding it in your hands. They are vital if you'll frequently watch movies or video chat with family and friends.

External keyboards. Planning to do a lot of typing on your tablet? Perhaps you'll want to use a physical keyboard instead of the virtual one on the screen. You can find some that connect wirelessly via Bluetooth or with a cable.

Bags. Frequent travelers may want a dedicated bag for their tablets. Some manufacturers make carryalls for specific tablets, and include pockets for chargers and cables.

Touch screen pens. Also known as styluses, use these to write and draw on the screen. They're excellent if you plan to use your tablet to take notes or create digital art.

Nothing is more important than keeping your tablet safe and secure. Here are a few of the best ways to ensure your device — and your personal information — is protected.

- Privacy settings. Go to your tablet's Settings app to check if apps are using your information or sharing your location data. Turn these off when possible.

- Antivirus apps. The App Store for Apple's iPads and the Google Play Store for Android tablets both have antivirus software you can download to your device. Type "antivirus" in the app store's search box to see available options.

- Parental control apps. These can prevent your tablet from accessing inappropriate material as well as limit the amount of time per day that people can use the device.

5 Android tablets

Android is an open source operating system, which means dozens of manufacturers can use it on their devices. And you'll find each company puts its own spin on their Android tablets. So one from Samsung may look a bit different from one made by Alcatel. Manufacturers also often add their own unique features and apps.

In addition, because Android can be installed on a range of devices, they all don't run on the same operating system version. When new updates are released, manufacturers may even opt out of updating their devices. That means not every tablet will be able to run the most recent version of Android. Usually, this is no cause for alarm. Yours will most likely still give you a great experience.

Just be aware certain functions, icons, and menu options could appear slightly different depending on which Android version and tablet you are using.

Shop talk: 2 factors guarantee tablet success

You have dozens of choices when shopping for a new Android tablet. And with several different manufacturers, it can be tough to decide on the device that's best for you. Consider these two attributes when you're researching what to buy.

Price. The cheapest Android tablets sell for under $100, while high-end ones clock in at well over $1,000. But what are you getting when you pay more cash? Better established brands may charge a bit extra just because of their name. And traditionally, more expensive tablets tend to be made of higher quality materials, have more storage space, and offer a faster, smoother experience.

Size. Tablets come in a wide range of dimensions. Some have screens that are smaller than 7 inches on the diagonal, but bigger models can measure well over 11 inches. And as the screen size increases, the tablet goes up in price. If you plan to use your tablet to watch movies or make video calls, it could be worth the extra cash for a larger screen. However, frequent travelers may decide that a smaller, more portable device is better.

Get started with a Google Account

Android is owned by the tech giant Google. So devices that use the Android operating system often come pre-installed with Google's apps — Gmail, Google Maps, and the Chrome web browser, for instance.

In order to get the most out of an Android tablet, you'll need to have an account with Google. If you already use Gmail, simply enter your login details for this when you first turn on a new tablet. If you do not have a Google Account, you can create one under several different circumstances.

- During the initial setup of your Android tablet, it may be mandatory to create a Google Account.

- When you open an app that requires a Google Account, you may be prompted to register with Google.

- You can also go to the Settings app and select Accounts and backup > Accounts > Add account.

Once you are cued to register a new Google Account, follow these steps to sign up.

1. Enter your first name and, optionally, your last name in the corresponding boxes. Tap on the *Next* button.

2. Enter your date of birth and gender. Press the *Next* button.

3. Create a username that you will use to sign in to your account. This should be something that you can easily remember. After you've chosen a username, press *Next*.

4. Create a password for the account. You will need to re-enter it for confirmation. Press *Next*.

5. A screen with your account details will be displayed. Tap the *Next* button to complete the sign-in to your new account.

Your Google Account is good for more than just setting up your tablet and logging in to apps.

- Access your account from any computer or mobile device via the internet. Go to *accounts.google.com*, log in, and — voila — you can connect to your Gmail, Google Drive, or other online service.

- Synchronize your content. Link your data so it is available from all of your web-enabled devices — whenever you sign in to your Google Account.

Home screen advantage: Essential info at your fingertips

The first thing you'll see when you turn on your tablet is the Home screen. Learn what everything is before you dive in and start using your device.

Favorites Tray. This is the area where you can place frequently used apps for quick access. To add apps to it, press and hold on an app's icon and drag it into the Favorites Tray. If you want to remove an app, press and hold on its icon, drag it into an empty space on the Home screen, then release it.

Search box. Use this to search either the web or the contents of your tablet. You can move it to a different location on your Home screen by pressing and holding it. Drag it to a new spot.

Notifications Area. Swipe down from this spot on your screen to view your current notifications.

Quick settings. This bar contains easy access to options for frequently changed settings, such as your Wi-Fi connection, display brightness, and volume. Swipe down on the screen to see more details.

Navigation bar. Sometimes these are physical buttons located on the body of your tablet. But more often, they are icons at the bottom of your Home screen. They are, from left to right:

- Back. Go to the most recently viewed item.

- Home. Return to the Home screen.

- Recent items. Display recently used apps.

Depending on the model of your tablet, you may be able to add more buttons and options to this bar. Some allow you to include controls for taking screenshots, opening the camera, and changing the volume.

Amazingly simple ways to customize your tablet

Want to add your own design stamp to your tablet? Fortunately, personalizing your device is a snap. Here's how to customize any Android tablet.

Tweak some basic settings. Use your Settings app to change how the tablet looks, sounds, and functions. Tap on this icon to open it.

- Display. Adjust the brightness of your tablet's screen, change the color theme, and fine-tune the size of words and icons on the screen.

- Sounds and Vibrations. Reset your tablet's volume and assign custom noises to alerts. For example, you can make the tablet play a specific sound when you receive an email. You can also mute alerts from this menu.

- Notifications. Toggle how notifications appear and which apps create notifications on your tablet's screen.

- Accounts and Backup. This menu helps you manage your Google Account, allows you to add multiple users and accounts to the tablet, and provides options for backing up your data.

Put up new wallpaper. Changing your tablet's wallpaper is a breeze. You can customize the image on your Lock or Home screen with these simple steps.

1. Press and hold on an empty area on the Home screen.

2. Tap on the *Wallpaper* button.

3. Tap on one of the options for setting a new wallpaper.

4. Choose an image you want to use and tap on it.

5. Press the *Set wallpaper* button. Choose if you want this image to be the background of your Home screen, your Lock screen, or both.

Quick — access Quick Settings. The Quick Settings area gives you a fast way to change little things on your phone. You can turn off Wi-Fi, activate your phone's battery saver mode, and more.

1. Find your Quick Settings by swiping down from the top of your screen.

2. To view more Quick Settings, swipe down again.

3. Tap on the + or *Pencil* button to edit your Quick Settings.

4. A panel with two sections will appear. One will show available buttons, while another will show your current Quick Settings options. Drag any button into your current Quick Settings to add it to this section. If you want to remove one, drag the button out of your current Quick Settings options.

How to become an app expert

Most Android tablets won't display all of your apps on the Home screen. Instead, you can only view a small selection of the programs that are on your device. But depending on your tablet, you can access a list of every app on your tablet by pressing the All Apps button or swiping up from the bottom of the screen. Simply tap on any app's icon to open it from this screen.

Press and hold on any app's icon to view more options. A small menu will appear with options that allow you to uninstall the app, add it to the Home screen, and more. You can also access App info by tapping on the lowercase "i" icon in the top right-hand corner of this menu. Use App info to disable or force stop an app if it is not working properly.

When you press and hold an app's icon, you can also drag it to add it to your Home screen or move it to a new spot on your All Apps page.

4 ways Chrome keeps you connected

Google Chrome is the default web browser for most Android tablets. If you want to use your device to surf the web, you'll need to know the ins and outs of this app.

Search like a pro. Use the bar at the top of a Chrome window to search by keywords or phrases. You can also type a web address — called a URL — into this bar to go directly to a website.

1. Enter text into the search bar.

2. Tap on the magnifying glass icon next to an item to view Google search results for that word or phrase.

3. Web addresses may appear in the drop down list while you are typing. If you want to go straight to that website, tap on the URL.

Save your favorite pages. Chrome can create virtual bookmarks so that you can quickly navigate to your favorite web pages. Here's how to add a new bookmark to your browser.

1. Go to any web page that you want to bookmark.

2. Tap on the star-shaped icon at the right-hand side of the search bar.

3. To view your bookmarks, tap on this menu button in the top, right-hand corner of your window. Select *Bookmarks* to see a list of your saved pages.

Multitask with tabs. Want to browse multiple web pages from a single window? Enter browser tabs. Just tap any tab at the top of your screen to swap between websites. To open a new tab, press on the + symbol in the top bar next to your current tab.

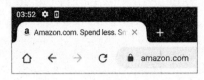

Tailor your settings. Maybe you want to tweak the default settings in Chrome to make your web browsing experience smoother. Tap on this icon in the top, right-hand corner of your window and select *Settings* to view your options.

Want to try a different web browser on your tablet? You can download other web-browsing apps from the Google Play Store. Enter "browsers" into the search box and scroll through your different options.

Maximize your Google search strategy

Google's search engine is heavily integrated into Android tablets. You can use the built-in search bar to browse the web or find apps and files on your device. Here are two ways to use this handy tool.

Text search. The most common way to use your tablet's search function? Just type text into the bar.

1. Tap in the Google search bar and start typing out a word, phrase, or name of an app you're looking for.

2. If an app appears in the list of suggested results, tap on it to open it on your tablet.

3. Press the magnifying glass icon next to the search results to perform a web search.

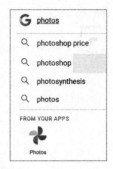

Cancel the search at any time by pressing on the x icon in the search bar.

Voice search. You can also use voice commands to open apps and search the web with Google. Simply tap on the microphone icon in the Google search box. When this screen appears, say the word or phrase you want to search for.

Never lose files or photos again

Want to make sure you never lose any of your favorite photos or important documents stored on your tablet? Then regularly create backups of your data.

Depending on your device, you may have a couple different ways to do this. Some manufacturers offer their own services and websites where you can back up your data. Many Android tablets, however, use Google One to save photos, apps, and files. Follow these steps to create a backup for your tablet using Google One.

1. Go to Settings > Google and tap on *Backup*. On some tablets you may need to go to Settings > System > Backup.

2. Tap the *Turn on* button.

3. Change the *Backup by Google One* slider to the on position.

4. Tap on the *Back up now* button to perform the initial backup. You can also turn on automatic backups so that you don't have to manually repeat this process.

6 iPads

An iPad is a great option if you're looking for an Apple device to read e-books, watch movies on the go, or video chat with family and friends. These tablets are smaller and lighter than laptops, but pack a bit more power and larger screens than smartphones.

iPad. Close to the original version of the iPad, it has a 10.2-inch screen and is the cheapest option in Apple's lineup.

iPad mini. Apple's smallest, lightest tablet, it has an 8.3-inch screen, which makes it great for frequent travelers or people who are more comfortable with a smaller device.

iPad Air. This option is about the same size as the standard iPad, but with a slightly larger screen and thinner body.

iPad Pro. This is Apple's most powerful tablet and comes in two sizes. While it is the most expensive option, it's a good choice if you're going to replace your laptop with a tablet.

Recent models can be used with the Apple Pencil — a stylus for writing and drawing directly on the screen, and Apple's Smart Keyboard.

Your iPad may have different features depending on which model you choose and the age of your device.

Stay up to date with iPadOS

Apple designed their tablet operating system — known as iPadOS — to set their iPads apart from their iPhones.

Every year, Apple releases a major update to iPadOS that offers big new features and changes to certain menu options and app icons. However, they also put out additional updates throughout the year. These smaller releases contain bug fixes and security improvements that are important to keep up with.

To see if your iPad needs an update, go to Settings > General > Software Update. Tap on the *Download and Install* button to start the update process.

You can also set your device to automatically download and install updates when they are available. Go to Settings > General > Software Update > Automatic Updates and change *Download iPadOS Updates* to *On*.

Tablet power: Settings give you ultimate control

When you first turn on a brand new iPad, you must go through the setup process. This helps your device connect to Wi-Fi, choose the correct language, and pinpoint your location. You can skip over these features or change them later using the Settings app.

You can also use Settings to customize your device and set it up just the way you want. To access Settings, tap this icon on the Home screen.

The app is divided into two sections.

- The left-hand sidebar contains the main categories. Click on any one of these categories to change its settings.

- The main window shows the item selected in the sidebar. Some options have slider buttons which can turn settings on or off. Tap the button to toggle between them.

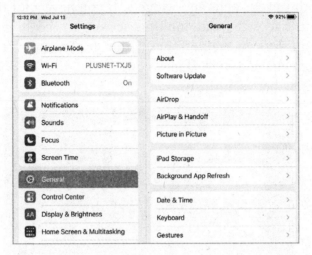

One smart Apple: Get started with an ID account

All iPads are linked to an Apple ID account. You need one to properly set up and use all the features on your device. If you don't already have one, there are a few different situations that will prompt you to create an Apple ID.

- during the initial setup process for a new iPad

- when you first access an app or service that requires an Apple ID, such as the App Store

- online at the Apple website — *appleid.apple.com*

You can access certain online features of your Apple account by using it to log in to *icloud.com*.

Create your perfect iPad Home screen

The first thing you see after starting up your iPad is your Home screen with various apps and widgets. If you have a lot of these tools, your iPad will create multiple screens to accommodate them. Small dots on the bottom of your display indicate how many of these screens you have. Tap on one of the dots or swipe left or right to cycle between them.

Here are a few tips for working with apps and Home screens.

- Press and hold on an app's icon to access a menu of options.

- Press and hold on an app's icon and then drag it to a new position on your Home screen. If the app's menu appears, hold down the app and drag it away from the menu until the icon begins to wobble. You can drag the app to the edge of the screen to move it to another Home screen.

- Press and hold on an app and tap the – button to remove it from your iPad. If you want to add deleted apps back to your iPad, go the App Store, search for the app, and tap on the cloud icon next to it. If you already paid for the app, it is free to download again.

- If you don't want to have multiple Home screens, press and hold a blank spot. When the icons begin to wobble, tap on the dots at the bottom of your screen. Thumbnails of your Home screens will be displayed. Tap on the check mark to toggle them on or off.

Take care when you're moving apps around on the Home screen. If you drag the icon too close to the edge, you might accidentally switch to another Home screen. Try holding the app near the middle of the screen while you decide where to put it.

3 time-saving features put you in the driver's seat

Need to change apps and settings on the fly? Get to know these three features and soon you'll be navigating your tablet like a pro.

The Dock. This bar at the bottom of the Home screen holds frequently used apps.

In iPadOS 16, the Dock is separated into two sections by a thin, vertical dividing line. The left side contains saved apps, and the right side shows recently used items and the App Library.

When you get a new iPad, the default saved apps are Messages, Safari, Music, Mail, Calendar, Photos, and Notes. However, you can change these easily.

- Add an app to the Dock by pressing and holding its icon on the Home screen. Drag it into the Dock and release.

- Remove an app from the Dock by pressing and holding on its icon. Drag it to the main area of the screen and release. Don't worry — this won't delete the app from your iPad. You can still find it on your Home screen or in the App Library.

The Dock is hidden when apps are open, but you can access it at any time. Do a short swipe up from the bottom of the screen to view it while using an app.

To customize the Dock, go to Settings > Home Screen & Multitasking.

Control Center. Swipe down from the top, right-hand corner of any screen to get fast access to this collection of useful functions and frequently used settings.

For instance, you can use the Control Center to change the screen brightness, take a photo, or turn on the iPad's flashlight. Change the options in the Control Center by going to Settings > Control Center.

App Switcher. This feature helps you quickly cycle through all apps on your iPad. Swipe up from the bottom of the screen and hold your finger down for a moment. A grid displaying all of your currently open apps will appear.

- Swipe left and right to view all of the apps.

- Tap on an app to make it full screen.

- Press on an app and drag it to the top of the screen to close it.

Control app chaos with the App Library

When you download a new app to your iPad, it automatically gets added to your Home screen. If there's no room on your original Home screen, your iPad simply creates another one.

Given the almost endless variety of apps available to download, you can see how easily your device could become overwhelmed with app icons and Home screens. That can make it almost impossible to organize your apps and find what you're looking for.

Fortunately, the App Library can help you clear up the clutter and streamline your tablet.

Tap on this icon in the Dock to open the App Library.

Or swipe from right to left past all your Home screens until you reach this screen.

Navigate by category. Apps in the App Library are automatically organized into categories or folders. Here are a few tips for finding things from this screen.

- Tap on any app's icon to open it. If there are more than four apps in a folder, you'll see a group of smaller icons shrunk into the bottom, right-hand corner of that folder. Tap this group of apps to view all the items in that category.

- Press and hold anywhere on the App Library screen to access the control buttons. Tap the x on the top, left-hand corner of an app to delete it from your iPad. Note that some apps cannot be removed.

Search for apps in a flash. To view all of the apps in the App Library alphabetically, tap on the search bar at the top of the screen.

- Swipe up or down to scroll through the list of apps. Tap on a letter in the sidebar to move to that section of the list.

- Type an app's name into the search bar to find it. The results will appear below the search bar.

Organize and focus: 3 tools amp up efficiency

Want to work on a few different apps at once? Multitasking is a snap on your iPad, as long as you know how to use these features.

Split View. Use this feature to view two app windows side by side. This makes working with multiple apps a breeze.

1. Open any app and tap on the three dots at the top of the window.

2. You'll see a menu showing the different window display options.

3. Tap on *Split View*.

4. Your first app is minimized. Tap on a second app in your Dock or Home screen.

5. The two apps are now displayed side by side.

If you don't want the two apps to be split evenly down the screen, you can tweak the size of each window. Simply drag the middle border between the apps to resize them.

Slide Over View. See two apps at the same time — one app displayed in full screen mode, the other as a floating window. Here's how to do it.

1. Open any app and tap on the three dots at the top of the window.

2. Tap on *Slide Over*.

3. The app is minimized. Tap on another app on the Dock or Home screen.

4. The second app you selected will open in full screen, and your original app will appear in a floating window on the right-hand side of your screen.

5. Press and hold the dots at the top of the floating window and drag it around your screen to reposition as needed.

Stage Manager. You can use this feature to view one app in the middle of your screen while still having quick access to everything else you have open. The open apps you are not using will be minimized on the side of your screen.

Tap this button in the Control Center to open Stage Manager. Note this feature is not available on all iPad models.

Simple steps make you a widgets whiz

Your iPad Home screen has more than just apps on it. The larger icons, known as widgets, show you current information from your favorite apps without having to open them. They're great for seeing the time, jotting down quick notes, or checking the weather. Tap on a widget to open the full version of its related app.

Up to 10 widgets can also be stacked together so you have more on one screen. Scroll vertically through a stack to view individual widgets.

Customize. Want to change the information that a widget shows or choose which widgets are in a stack? Simply press and hold on any widget to access its menu options.

You can easily change where the widgets are on your Home screen, too. Press and hold on a widget and drag it to a new spot.

Add. Your iPad comes equipped with a few default widgets. But you can easily add more to your Home screen. Here's how.

1. Press and hold on an empty area of your Home screen until the app icons and widgets begin to wobble.

2. Tap the + button in the top, left-hand corner of the screen.

3. In the widgets gallery, you'll see a full list of available widgets on the left-hand sidebar. Type into the search bar at the top of the window to find a specific widget.

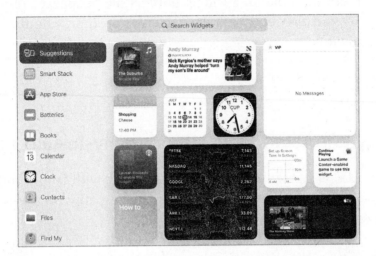

4. Tap on a widget in the sidebar to view more options in the main window. You can swipe from right to left, or tap on the dots near the bottom of the window, to view different options for the widget's size and settings.

5. Tap on the *Add Widget* button to add it to your Home screen.

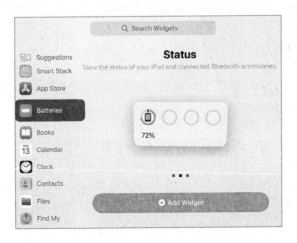

Delete. If you need to free up space on your iPad's screen, you may decide to remove a few widgets.

1. Press and hold on a widget until its menu appears. Tap on *Remove Widget*. If you don't see this prompt, you may need to tap *Edit Widget*.

2. Tap on *Remove*.

Stay connected with these easy-to-use apps

Your iPad is a great tool for staying in touch with family and friends. Here are a few tips for using the best apps for messaging and emailing.

Mail. This is the iPad's default app for all of your email needs.

If you have an account with another email provider, like Google or Yahoo, it's easy to add it to this app. Here's how.

1. Go to Settings > Mail and tap *Accounts*.

2. Tap *Add Account* and select your email provider.

3. Enter your email address and password.

4. If you see *Next*, tap on it and wait for Mail to verify your account.

5. If you see the *Save* button, tap it to finish the setup process.

A new feature in iPadOS 16 lets you take back emails that you sent by mistake. Simply tap on the *Undo Send* button at the bottom of the Mail window. However, this option is only available for 10 seconds after sending an email.

Messages. Use this app to send text messages from your iPad.

A new feature will let users edit some messages after they have been sent to fix typos or other mistakes. To do this, press and hold on the message you want to edit. Tap on the *Edit* button.

This option is available for 15 minutes after the message has been sent. You can also press *Undo Send* to take back messages sent in error.

The search for answers: Spotlight and Siri

Hunting through your iPad for the right app or file can be tricky. But with a few tricks, you can find anything you're looking for in a jiffy. Here are two of the fastest, easiest ways to search on your tablet.

Spotlight Search. Press and drag down on any empty space of your Home screen to bring up this search bar. Use Spotlight to find apps, contacts, and other content on your iPad, and even search the web.

Siri. This is Apple's digital voice assistant. You can activate Siri by saying "Hey Siri" or by pressing the Home button or top button of your iPad. If Siri doesn't respond, you may need to set it up.

1. Open the Settings app.

2. Go to *Siri & Search*.

3. Toggle *Listen for "Hey Siri"* to the on position.

4. Follow the prompts on the screen to train Siri to recognize your voice.

Want to get more done? Use these free apps

Your iPad comes equipped with several default apps that are great ways to stay organized and productive. Here's how to use them to stay on top of your everyday activities.

Calendar. Stay up to date with your events and appointments.

Contacts. Create entries for friends, family members, and other contacts so you can quickly send them texts, emails, or find their phone number.

Notes. Great for making lists and jotting down quick thoughts. You can include photos, videos, and links to websites in these notes, too.

Reminders. Set up virtual reminders so you don't forget important events or appointments.

Maps. Look up stores, restaurants, and other destinations then get step-by-step directions to them.

Clock. Check the time anywhere in the world, set timers, or create alarms. There is a stopwatch function, too.

Voice Memos. Record voice notes without having to type text into an app.

Find more free Apps for your iPad in the App Store. Tap on this icon to access it.

Stay on top of your device's security to make sure your data is safe. To access an iPad's security features, go to Settings > Privacy & Security. Then specify which apps can access your data and your location.

There is a also a function called App Privacy Report. When you turn it on, you create a weekly report of which apps access your data, your location, your camera, and microphone.

Top 10 Tips for Tablets

1. A tablet is a great choice if you want a device that offers a good-sized screen and portability. They're excellent for travelers and people who make frequent video calls.

2. A cover and a screen protector can save your tablet from bumps, scrapes, and drops.

3. Download an antivirus app for your tablet to keep it safe and secure.

4. Tech companies offer a number of accessories, such as stands and keyboards. Think carefully about how you'll use your tablet before you buy expensive add-ons.

5. You'll need to create a Google Account to make sure you get the most out of using an Android tablet.

6. Use the Google search options to find anything on your tablet in a flash. You can even use the voice search so you don't have to type out questions.

7. Back up data on your Android tablet using Google One. You'll never lose your favorite files, photos, or videos.

8. Set up an Apple ID to use all of your iPad's features plus Apple's online services.

9. Turn off some of your iPad's Home screens to keep your display clean and clutter-free.

10. Check for updates to your iPadOS by going to Settings > General > Software Update.

Smartphones

7 Smarter smartphone shopping

The growth in smartphone usage is astounding. Just think, back in 2011, only about 35% of adults in the U.S. owned one. That number is now well over 85%. But despite their popularity, most people say that their smartphone is their single most frustrating tech device.

It's easy to understand why. Manufacturers are adding more and more bells and whistles each year, making the phones harder to use. Just remember though, you're not dumb — it's your device that's not so smart. After all, it needs you to tell it what to do. Once you familiarize yourself with the ins and outs of using a smartphone, you'll be making calls, surfing the web, and sending texts like a pro.

Ready to shop? Dial in to top phone features

Shopping for a new phone can get confusing. After all, you're constantly bombarded with tech terms and flashy features on phones that cost hundreds of dollars. But if you want to cut through all the jargon, these common terms can help you narrow down what to look for.

Operating system. This is the name for the software that powers your phone. The two biggest mobile operating systems are Google's Android and Apple's iOS. If you use a Windows computer or an Android tablet, you may prefer an Android phone. If you're an Apple fan, you might want to choose an iPhone.

Carrier. The company that provides your cell service — which lets you make phone calls and send texts — is known as your carrier.

Most major companies, like AT&T and Verizon, offer plans that give you a monthly allowance of minutes, texts, and data.

Data. A smartphone requires an internet connection to download emails, connect to the web, and stream music or videos. When you don't have a Wi-Fi connection, your phone will use data. For example, you may pay for 5 gigabytes of data per month.

Display. This is the term used for a smartphone's screen. Some phones offer super bright, high resolution displays. That means the pictures and text look sharper. But these screens are more expensive. Bigger screens tend to cost more, too.

Refresh rate. Smartphones are constantly flashing new pictures on the screen. When you scroll through an app or watch a video, these changes are happening dozens of times per second. Higher refresh rates make the animations on your screen appear smoother — but they drive up the price of the phone.

Camera. Smartphones often have a front-facing camera for taking pictures of yourself — called selfies — or for video chats. In addition, they can have several rear cameras for higher quality pictures and angles. If you frequently take pictures with your phone, you may want to opt for one with an ultra-wide angle lens that gets more in the frame, or a telephoto lens that lets you zoom further in.

Battery capacity. This determines how long you can use your phone before it needs to be charged again. Look for a phone with a larger battery so you can go longer between charges. Some companies also have fast charging phones, which let you top off your phone's battery in just a few minutes.

7 critical questions to ask before laying down cash

Most smartphones will last for several years. Eventually, though, you're going to need to replace it. But before you break out your wallet, ask yourself these important questions. The answers could wind up saving you hundreds — or even thousands — of dollars.

Are there software updates? If you want to make your outdated smartphone feel brand new again, check your Settings app to see if there is an update available. Installing the newest operating system on your phone can help fix bugs, make the phone seem faster, and even offer more protection against hackers. And as an added bonus, updating your phone is free.

Is it obsolete? As smartphones get older, manufacturers stop supporting updates and fixes for the device. That means it can no longer be updated to the newest version of the operating system. This can prevent you from getting important security updates or bug fixes. Most phones are usually supported for about 5 years, but this can vary depending on the manufacturer and the operating system. Check with the manufacturer to see if your device is still supported.

Do you have a warranty? If your phone is within its warranty period, the manufacturer may foot the bill to replace it or fix it. Read the fine print though, since not all types of damage are covered under every warranty. Contact the phone's manufacturer if you have questions.

Is it worth fixing? A repair bill for your smartphone may be expensive, but a new device could easily cost more. Find out if the repairs will be less than buying a new phone.

Can you find a deal on an older model? Companies release brand new smartphones every year. And these flagship models can cost well over $1,000. But you don't need to buy the latest if you're ready for an upgrade. Look for discounts on phones that are a year or two old. They may offer features your current phone lacks — without breaking the bank.

Do you really need a new phone? Slick marketing campaigns make the latest and greatest smartphones seem like must-have devices. Before you shell out the moola to upgrade, consider whether or not your current phone still meets all your needs.

Will new features justify the expense? New phones usually promise brand new features, better battery life, or major upgrades. Then it comes down to whether or not you want the features on the latest models. Some may dramatically change your smartphone experience. Others can just be fun to have.

Want to get the best deal when you're shopping for a smartphone? Price comparison websites can help you track down sales and discounts so you never pay full price again. Check them out.

- *Shopsavvy.com*

- *Pricegrabber.com*

- *Shopping.com*

- *Shopzilla.com*

Tap, drag, and pinch: Brush up on 5 basic motions

You must learn how to get around your smartphone's touch screen if you want to use all of the features you paid for. Here are a few simple gestures to get you started.

- Tap on an app's icon to open it.

- Press and hold on the icon to open the app's menu and view more options.

- Move an app around the Home screen by pressing and holding on it, then dragging it to a new position.

- Double tap on a web page or photo to zoom in. Repeat the process to go back to your original view.

- Place your thumb and forefinger close together on the screen and slowly slide them apart to zoom in on documents, photos or web pages. Move them back together to zoom out.

The sudden realization that you can't find your phone is super stressful. You may have lost your device, or — even worse — someone stole it. But never fear. With a little know-how, you can locate your smartphone fast.

Most modern phones come equipped with a feature called Find my Phone, which you can use to track down a missing device. To start, simply link your phone with an Apple ID or Google Account.

Then, if you misplace your device, the Find My Phone app attempts to locate it and show you where it is on a map. This feature will also play an alarm or ring tone on the phone so you can track it by sound. For more peace of mind, know you can remotely lock it to prevent thieves from stealing your data.

2 secrets keep your phone safe and sound

Your smartphone goes nearly everywhere you do. Chances are it's never far from your hand, purse, or pocket. But this portability means that your device is prone to scratches, scrapes, drops, and bumps.

Want to avoid an expensive repair bill or even the high cost of a replacement phone? Invest in a little bit of protection now.

- A smartphone case offers defense against damage. Even if it makes your thin and sleek phone a bit bulkier, it will also make it easier to hold.

- Consider a screen protector, too. Most are made of plastic or tempered glass and are virtually invisible. But they still protect your expensive touch screen from scratches or cracks.

4 signs your phone has been hacked — and what to do about it

You use your smartphone for practically everything now — including snapping photos of family, shopping online, and banking. That means you're storing personal data on your phone, too. No surprise, then, that phones are a prime target for criminals looking to steal your info. Here are four signs that you've been hacked.

- Pop-up ads frequently appear all over your screen.

- App icons immediately disappear after you install them.

- Your battery life seems much shorter than usual. The phone may even die shortly after being fully charged.

- You see apps that you don't remember installing.

If you notice any of these warning flags, don't panic. You can download antivirus apps from your phone's app store to help protect your phone and prevent future viruses.

8 Android smartphones

The tech giant Google owns Android, but they license it out to dozens of different manufacturers. Each company puts their own spin on this mobile operating system. That means an Android phone from Samsung may come with a unique look and slightly different default apps from an LG Android phone.

Because Android comes on a wide variety of phones, they might not all run the same version of this operating system. And manufacturers may decide against upgrading to the newest version on their devices.

However, you'll still get a smooth, easy-to-use experience no matter what Android smartphone you are using. Just be aware that certain functions, icons, and menu options may appear slightly different than described here.

Home sweet Home screen: 5 fundamentals you must know

The Home screen is the first thing you'll see when you turn on your Android phone. If you want to navigate your device like a pro, it helps to know what everything is.

Favorites Tray. The row of icons near the bottom of the screen are for quick access to frequently used apps.

Search box. Use this to search the web or find things on your phone. Move it to a different location on your screen by pressing on it and dragging it to a new spot.

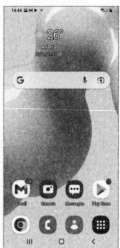

Notifications Area. Swipe down from the top, left-hand corner to view alerts and notifications on your phone.

Quick settings. Swipe down from the top, right-hand corner to view frequently changed settings, like volume and screen brightness.

Navigation buttons. These appear at the bottom of the Home screen. They are, from left to right:

- Recents. View all your currently open apps.

- Home. Return to the Home screen from any app.

- Back. View your previously used app.

Restyle your phone to make it feel brand new

Manufacturers all put their own design touches on Android smartphones, but with a little know-how, you can change the default look.

To customize the background image, the theme, and other elements of your device, press and hold on any blank space in the Home screen. A menu will appear that will let you personalize your phone.

Wallpaper. Tap on the *Wallpapers* button to change the background image on your Home Screen, Lock screen, or both.

Themes. Tap on the *Themes* button to view all kinds of styles you can apply to your phone. Themes add custom color schemes to your phone's menu bars, buttons, icons, and other elements.

Widgets. Think of widgets as tiny windows into your apps. They're always running, so they can provide information at a glance. Widgets are great for keeping track of mail, sports scores, news headlines, or the local weather.

1. Tap on the *Widgets* button.

2. Swipe up and down to view all of your phone's available widgets.

3. Press and hold on a widget, then drag it to the Home screen to add it. To move a widget around your Home screen, press and hold on it. Drag it to a new spot.

Switch to gesture navigation — it's fun and efficient

Recent versions of Android have a feature that lets you use a series of swiping gestures so it's quicker and easier to access your Home screen. Here's how to turn this on.

1. Open the Settings app and select *Display*.

2. Tap on the *Navigation bar* option.

3. Tap the *Swipe gestures* button.

On some phones, you may need to access this option by going to Settings > System > Gestures.

Now, instead of the standard navigation buttons at the bottom of your Home screen, you should see a small bar. Use these commands to navigate your phone.

- Swipe up on the bar to return to your Home screen.

- Swipe inwards from the edge of the screen to go back.

- Swipe up from the Navigation bar and hold your finger on the screen to view recently used apps.

You wouldn't leave your house unattended and unlocked, would you? So why leave your phone laying around unguarded. Setting up a Lock screen is a vital way to protect the information on your device.

1. Open the Settings app and tap on the *Lock screen* option.

2. Select *Screen lock type*.

3. Pick an option for unlocking your phone. You can choose from Swipe, Pattern, PIN, and Password on all Android phones. Some devices may also offer the option for a Fingerprint scan or a Face scan.

4. After you choose an unlock option, follow the instructions on the screen to finish setting it up. You'll now use this method to open your phone from the Lock screen.

Get app happy in 3 easy steps

Apps are key to doing almost anything on your smartphone. You'll use them to make calls, browse the web, send emails, and more. So before you can become an expert at using your phone, you'll need to master apps. Here are a few skills to start with.

- Tap on any app's icon to open it.

- Press and hold on any app's icon to view a menu of options.

- Press and hold an app's icon and drag it around the Home screen to move it to a new location. You can switch it to another Home screen by moving it to the edge of your display.

If you have more apps than your phone's single Home screen can show, your phone will automatically create another Home screen. You can switch between them by swiping left or right on your display to see all these apps.

Scroll through every app on your phone by using the All Apps section. Swipe up from the bottom of the screen or tap this button.

Keep favorite apps close with this quick hack

You want to keep apps that you use on a regular basis in an easy-to-reach spot on your phone. That's where the Favorites Tray comes in. This row at the bottom of every Home screen houses frequently used apps so that you can get to them in a flash. You can change them out at any time.

- To add an app to the Favorites Tray, press and hold any app's icon on the Home screen. Drag it to the Favorites Tray. If there is not enough space, the app will remain in its original location.

- To remove an app, press and hold on its icon. Drag it from the Favorites Tray to an empty area on the Home screen. This won't delete the app from your phone.

Contacts app helps you stay in touch

No need to keep an address book if you have a smartphone. Your Android comes equipped with the Contacts app, which you can use to store phone numbers and email addresses for hundreds of people. Here are a few tips for using this simple app.

Add contacts. Want to save someone's contact information? Here's how to add a new entry.

1. Tap on this icon to open the Contacts app.

2. Tap on the + button in the top, right-hand corner of your screen.

3. Decide where to store this contact's information. You can save it directly to your phone, put it on your SIM card so you can transfer contacts when you get a new device, or save it on Google so you can sync it between your computer, tablet, and smartphone.

4. Enter the details for your new contact and tap the *Save* button.

Access your contacts. After you've added people to your contacts list, use the Contacts app to reach out with the press of a button.

- Open the Contacts app then tap on the magnifying glass in the top, right-hand corner to find a specific contact.

- Tap on this button in the top, left-hand corner to manage your contacts.

- Tap on a contact to see more details. You can also use the buttons on their contact page to call them, send a text message, or start a video call.

Geena Green 🛈

Phone 07777 123456

Make calls with ease: 3 steps show you how

Your smartphone can surf the web, send emails, and snap photos. But its main purpose is to make calls. Here are a few tips to help you use your phone.

Type in a number. Want to call a new number — one that's not in your contact list? Here's how to bring up your phone's keypad.

1. Tap on the Phone app.

2. Select the *Keypad* button at the bottom of the screen. Enter the phone number you want to call.

3. Tap on the *Call* button.

Phone   + Q ⋮

07779 876543

1	2 ABC	3 DEF
4 GHI	5 JKL	6 MNO
7 PQRS	8 TUV	9 WXYZ
*	0 +	#

Search for a contact. If you have somebody's number saved in your Contacts, you don't need to type out their digits to make a call. Simply search for them right from the Phone app. Here's how.

1. Open the Phone app.

2. Tap on the *Contacts* tab.

3. Scroll through the entries to find the Contact you are looking for. Or tap the search box and type out their name.

4. Select the Contact you want to call and view their details. Press the phone icon to make a call.

Navigate the call screen. After a call goes through, these buttons will appear at the bottom of your screen.

- Press the *Keypad* button to select numbers during automated calls or to dial an extension.

- Tap on the *Speaker* button to activate speakerphone. This will allow you to hear and speak without holding your phone close to your face.

- Select this button to end the call.

At any time you can access your Home screen and other apps without ending the call. Press the Home button to minimize the call and navigate to whatever app you need. Open the call screen again by tapping the partial window at the top of your screen or flipping through your open apps.

If you receive a call from an unknown number, it's often best not to answer it just in case it's a scam. The caller can always leave a voicemail, in which case you can listen to that before deciding whether or not you want to call back. You can also search the internet for their number to see if it's related to a known scammer.

Incoming call? Answer it lickety-split

When somebody calls you, your phone will play a ringtone and the number or contact details will appear on your screen. You can choose to answer or decline.

- Tap this button to accept the call.

- Tap this button to send the call to voicemail.

If you're using another app when someone calls you, this banner will appear at the top of your screen. You can simply tap on *Answer* or *Decline*.

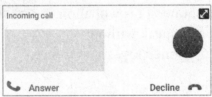

Personalize your ringtone: Make your phone more you

Nearly everyone has a smartphone these days. When a phone rings in public, it can be hard to know if it's yours or somebody else's. Fortunately, you can customize your ringtone to help curb that confusion.

1. Open the Settings app and tap on *Sounds and vibration*.

2. Select *Ringtone*.

3. Choose a new sound to play when you receive a phone call. You can tap on an option to hear a preview.

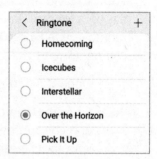

4. When you've chosen your favorite, press the + button to set it as your phone's default ringtone.

Can't find a ringtone you like in the options list? Download more choices from the Google Play Store. Go to the Play Store and type "ringtones" into the search box.

3 all-important keyboard commands

Even if you're an expert typist, you may stumble when it comes to your phone's keyboard. The most basic buttons and commands often vary from a normal keyboard. Here are three you need to know.

1. Tap to capitalize a single letter. Tap twice to activate Caps Lock.

2. Tap to view numbers and symbols. Tap again to return to letters.

3. Tap to delete a character.

Depending on your specific smartphone, certain options and keyboard buttons may appear slightly different. You can also go to the Google Play Store to download other keyboards, such as Google's Gboard.

Want to send photos or videos in a text message? Large files can eat up a lot of data if you're only using a cell signal. Go over your monthly data limit and your cell carrier may hit you with a hefty charge. Here's how to check how much data you've used.

1. Open the Settings app.

2. On some Android phones you'll tap *Network & Internet* and choose the *Internet* option. Then tap *Settings* next to your mobile carrier's name. On other Androids, you'll tap *Connections* then *Data usage*.

3. At the top of the page, you should see how much total data you have used. Select *App data usage* or *Mobile data usage* to see how much data you use over a chosen time period. Check which apps use the most data.

If you don't have a lot of data left for the month, you may want to wait until you're connected to Wi-Fi before you send images, videos, or other large files.

How to text with the best

Cellphone users worldwide send over 18.7 billion text messages every single day. It's easy to see why. Texting is a great way to communicate quickly and easily. If you're not an expert texter, don't worry. These simple tips will help you send messages with ease.

Send a text message. Follow these steps to create and send the perfect text.

1. Open the Messages app on your phone.

2. Tap the new message icon in the lower-right corner of your screen.

3. Enter a phone number or tap the + button to choose a contact you want to text.

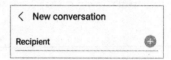

4. Enter the text for the message and press this button to send the message.

You can also text someone right from your Contacts app. Simply press this icon next to their details.

Add emoji. These small digital icons are used to express emotions and are a great way to add some flavor to your texts. Here's how to add them to your messages.

1. Tap the emoji symbol on your keyboard.

2. The default emoji are displayed. View more by tapping on one of the categories located on the top toolbar or by swiping through the screen.

3. Once you find an emoji you want to use, tap it to add it to a text message.

Never download apps to your phone from anything other than your device's default app store. Items from third-party websites, emails, or text messages could contain viruses or other malicious software.

Add new apps: Learn and play on the go

The Google Play Store is home to nearly 3.5 million apps. There are ones that will let you track the weather, stay up to date with the news, and more. Here's how to find new apps for your phone.

1. Tap on the Play Store app.

2. The Play Store home page shows suggested apps below the tab labeled *For you*. To view more, tap on the *Apps* button on the bottom toolbar.

3. Scroll up and down to view more options. You can tap an app's name or icon to view more details about it.

4. To find certain types of apps, select the *Categories* button on the top toolbar.

5. Look for specific apps, topics, or categories by using the search box at the top of the Play Store window.

6. After locating an app you want to add to your phone, select the *Install* button to begin downloading it.

9 iPhones

Apple releases a shiny, new iPhone every year. The reason? It's good for business. But just because there's an all-new smartphone doesn't mean you need to buy it to get access to new features. The iPhone's operating system — iOS — comes out with major updates every year, too. And you can install them even if your iPhone is four or five years old.

Depending on your current phone and which version of iOS you have, certain menu items, icons, and functions may appear different.

4 secrets to iPhone control

Get to know four of the most important — but basic — iPhone features and functions.

Dock. This special area at the bottom of every Home screen houses frequently used apps for quick access. You can store up to four items here. To add an app to your Dock, press and hold on its icon, then drag it onto the Dock. To remove one, press, hold, and drag it off the Dock.

App Switcher. This feature displays all your currently open apps and lets you flip between them with ease.

1. Swipe up from the bottom of your screen to open the App Switcher.

2. Swipe left and right to view your open apps. Tap on any one to make it full screen.

3. Swipe up on any app to close it.

4. To exit the App Switcher and return to your Home screen, tap above or below the displayed apps.

App Library. Your Home screen can only hold so many apps. If you want to see them all listed in one place, use the iPhone's App Library. Simply swipe from right to left until you reach this screen.

Your apps will be grouped by categories. If a category has too many apps to show them all as large icons, tap on the bottom, right-hand corner of the category for a complete list.

You can also tap the search bar at the top of the screen to view an alphabetical list of every app on your phone. Tap on an app's icon to open it directly.

Home screens. When your default Home screen runs out of space, your iPhone automatically creates a new page — and so on. But don't worry, if you don't want to swipe through dozens of Home screens, you can hide certain pages.

1. Press and hold on a Home screen until the icons begin to wobble.

2. Tap on these dots just above the Dock.

3. All of your Home screen pages will display as thumbnails.
    Decide which one you'd like to hide, and tap the circle
    under it.

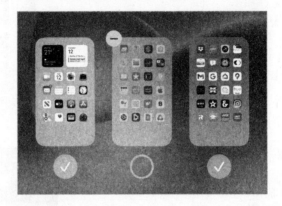

If a Home screen is hidden, you can only access the apps on it
through the App Library. You also need to have at least one Home
screen turned on at all times.

Perfect your experience with wonderful widgets

Think of widgets as mini apps. These little windows show info at a
glance, so you can check the weather or a stock price without having to open up a webpage or full app.

Add widgets. Here's how to add them to your iPhone.

1. Press and hold a blank area on your Home screen.

2. Tap the + button in the top, left-hand corner of the screen.

3. You'll see a list of all available widgets. Swipe up to scroll through the list.

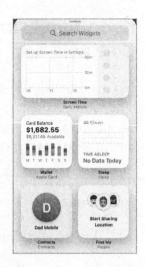

4. Tap on any widget you want to add to your Home screen. Swipe left and right to view different sizes and options for the widget.

5. Press *Add Widget*.

Move widgets. Move widgets around your Home screen by pressing and dragging the icon to a new spot. If you want to remove a widget, press and hold on it. Tap on *Remove Widget* when the menu appears.

View favorite widgets. *Today View* is a page that shows at-a-glance info from your most-used apps — without having them pinned to your Home screen. Get to it by swiping from left to right past all your Home screens.

Scroll to the bottom of this page and tap the *Edit* button to customize which widgets appear in this panel.

Keep family and friends close with Contacts app

No need for an old-fashioned address book if you own an iPhone. The Contacts app is a convenient way to store all their info — phone numbers, email addresses, and even important dates like birthdays or anniversaries.

Add contacts. Follow these simple steps to add contacts to your phone.

1. Tap on the Contacts app.

2. Press the + button in the top, right-hand corner.

3. Enter the contact details as well as other info, such as a birthday or nickname.

4. Tap the *Done* button to save the information.

If someone calls you, but they're not in your Contacts app, there's an easy way to add their info to your phone. Open the Phone app and tap the *Recents* button.

Tap the small i button to the right of the phone number and select *Create New Contact*.

Streamline your contacts. It's easy to create duplicate entries in the iOS Contacts app without meaning to. But a new feature helps you find these copies and merge them into a single entry.

1. Open the Contacts app. If your phone finds copies of the same contact, you should see a *Duplicates found* banner at the top of your screen.
   Tap on it.

Duplicates Found	70 >

2. Select an entry that has multiple contacts.

3. Tap on the *Merge* button at the bottom of the window. Press it again to confirm.

Talk to me: Answer calls even in lock mode

Incoming calls will look different depending on what you are doing at the time of the call. If you are using any of your apps on your phone, the caller details will appear as a banner at the top of the window. Simply tap the green, right-hand icon to answer the phone, or select the red, left-hand button to decline the call.

When your iPhone is locked, incoming calls will take up the whole screen. Swipe the bottom bar from left to right to answer the phone.

If you don't want to answer the call, you can set a reminder to call them back with the *Remind Me* button or send a text to the caller with the *Message* button.

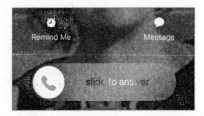

Personalize your ringtone in 4 foolproof steps

If everybody uses the same default ringtone, you may reach for your phone whenever the chime starts to play in public or even on a TV show. One way to make sure you don't get confused? Set up your own customized ringtone.

1. Open the *Settings* app.

2. Tap on *Sounds & Haptics* and select *Ringtone*.

3. Tap on a ringtone to select it. You'll hear a preview of the sound.

4. Press the *Back* button in the top, left-hand corner to save your selection.

The *Sounds & Haptics* menu also has options to change the alert sound and vibration settings for text messages, emails, and notifications.

Keyboard tricks get you typing like a pro

Your smartphone is a great tool for sending messages, jotting down notes, or writing a quick email. But before you can do all of these tasks, you must learn the virtual keyboard. Here are a few tips and tricks to make the most of this tool.

1. Tap to switch between capital and lowercase letters. Double-tap to turn on caps lock.

2. Tap to switch to a numbers and symbols keyboard.

3. Tap and hold to access Keyboard settings or turn on One-Hand mode.

4. Tap to delete letters.

5. Tap to start a new line.

6. Tap to turn on speech-to-text.

Customize your typing experience. Another way to access the Keyboard settings is by going to Settings > General > Keyboard. Here are some of your options.

- *Auto-Capitalization* automatically inserts a capital letter at the start of a new sentence.

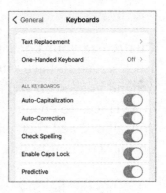

- *Auto-Correction* fixes misspelled words.

- *Predictive* suggests words on the bar above the keyboard.

Edit text double quick. Want to make changes to something you just typed out? Simply press or double-tap on a single word to

select it. Once a word is
selected, drag the cursor to
select more words or letters.
After you make a selection, a
menu will appear above your
cursor that gives you more
editing options.

Unlock secrets to a custom Lock screen

Your phone is home to a lot of private data. You don't want anyone
off the street able to pick up your iPhone and flip through your
info. That's where the Lock screen comes in. This feature provides
a secure landing page that requires your Face ID or a passcode to
unlock the phone. To set up a Lock screen, go to Settings > Face
ID & Passcode.

The latest iOS updates offer more than just security for the Lock
screen, though. Here are some of the brand new features.

Customize your Lock screen. Set up your
Lock screen to have different fonts and background images, so you'll recognize your iPhone
at a glance. To change these features, unlock
your phone and then press and hold anywhere
on the screen until this menu appears.

1. Tap on the *Customize* button.

2. Choose an area of the Lock screen to customize.

3. Tap on it and select a font style and color. Change the intensity of the selected color by dragging the slider underneath the color options.

4. When you're satisfied with your changes, tap the *Done* button in the top, right-hand corner to save your settings.

View widgets at a glance. Want to see sports scores, weather, or other info without unlocking your iPhone? A new iOS feature lets you add widgets to your iPhone's Lock screen.

1. Unlock your phone, press and hold on an area of the screen and tap on the Widgets box, which is just below the clock.

2. Tap on the widgets you want to add. You can choose from things like alarms, time zones, and your calendar.

2 new solutions for texting woes

Texting via the Messages app is one of the most popular ways to communicate today. And thanks to a brand new iPhone feature, you can edit — or even unsend — texts for up to 15 minutes after you've hit Send. You'll never have to worry about typos or texting the wrong person again.

- Press and hold on the text message you want to change. When the menu appears, tap the *Edit* button. Make changes to the text and tap the checkmark symbol to finalize them.

- Press and hold on the text message you want to take back. Then press the *Undo Send* button.

Editing text messages only works if you're messaging another Apple user. And you may not be able to make changes to sent messages if the person you're texting is using a different version of iOS.

Get the picture: Let emoji perk up your texts

Emoji are a great way to add a bit of flair and personality to a text message or an email. You have hundreds of different icons, facial expressions, and pictures to choose from, if you know where to look. Follow these simple steps to find them.

1. While writing a text or email, tap this icon on the bottom toolbar.

2. You'll see an emoji window.

3. Swipe from right to left to view more.

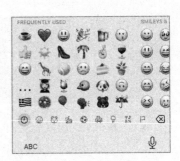

4. Press and hold on an emoji for different options — such as various skin tones or color themes.

5. Tap on an emoji to add it to a message.

6. Tap the *ABC* button on the bottom toolbar to return to the standard keyboard layout.

Concerned about spending too much time on your iPhone? You're not alone. Some experts estimate the average American whiles away over 5 hours every day on their smartphones.

Fortunately, you can track exactly how much screen time you're getting with Screen Time reports. Go to Settings > Screen Time and use this menu to set up daily logs, place restrictions on certain apps, manage downtimes when you can't look at your phone, and block inappropriate content.

Top 10 Tips for Smartphones

1. Before you upgrade to the latest, high-end smartphone, find out if your existing phone's software is current. Major updates are a free way to make your old phone feel good as new.

2. Consider buying last year's model if you must upgrade your phone. You'll get plenty of new features at a fraction of the price.

3. Use the Find My Phone function to track down your device if it is lost or stolen.

4. Set up a Lock screen to prevent anyone else from accessing the contents of your smartphone.

5. Customize the look and feel of your Android smartphone directly from the Home screen.

6. The Favorites Tray on an Android phone gives you quick access to the apps you use most frequently.

7. Use the Google Play Store to get new apps for your Android smartphone. Never download apps from unknown websites, text messages, or emails.

8. Swipe up from the bottom of your iPhone's Home screen to view the App Switcher. This feature lets you quickly cycle through all your open apps.

9. Customize your iPhone Lock screen and add widgets for up-to-date info on things like sports scores and the weather.

10. Use the Edit function on iPhones to change messages after you've sent them. Often you can unsend messages and emails shortly after they have been sent.

Your Devices

10 Customization

Tech companies offer an extensive range of devices, apps, and accessories. All these choices mean that the operating systems and user experience can vary wildly. But no matter what brand of smartphone you buy or what operating system your computer runs, you'll always have access to the Settings app.

This feature gives you numerous options for setting up and customizing your devices, so you can truly personalize your tech. Regardless of what device you're using, you can usually access the Settings menu by pressing on the gear icon. The exact design may vary from brand to brand.

Settings: Change, customize, and control your computer

Want to tweak your desktop or laptop? You'll need to open up the Settings app by clicking on the gear icon located near the bottom of your screen.

- If you're using a Windows computer, look for this icon on the Taskbar or in the Start menu.

- Mac users should see this icon somewhere on the Dock. If you're on Ventura or later, this app is called System Settings. However older versions of macOS may refer to it as System Preferences.

Expert path to personalizing your mobile device

Tablets and smartphones share a lot of the same icons and app names. That means the Settings app will probably look the same on an Android tablet and an Android smartphone. The same is true for iPhones and iPads. Here's how to find Settings on your mobile device.

- Android users will tap this icon to open Settings. It is often located in the Favorites Tray at the bottom of your screen. If you don't see it there, swipe up from the bottom of your screen to open the All Apps section and search for Settings.

- Apple users should tap this icon to view Settings. If it is not in the Dock at the bottom of your screen, swipe up from the bottom to open Spotlight. Type "Settings" into the search box to find the app.

Navigate the Settings menu with ease

Perhaps you have a smartphone, a tablet, and a computer — plus a handful of other devices. While they're all pretty different, the Settings menu is often set up the same way. You have two panels on the screen. The left-hand side displays the main categories, while the main window shows all the options contained in your selected category.

In some cases, you may have subcategories and menu options in your main window. To view these, click on the right-facing arrow next to a menu option. If you need to go back to the previous menu, you can do it a few different ways.

- Click or tap one of the main categories on the left-hand panel.

- Click or tap the left-facing arrow, or *Back* button, to return to your previous page.

In some Settings apps, your full path is displayed at the top of the main window. This shows which pages and menus you have gone through. You can click or tap one of the options in this path to go directly to that page.

System › Sound › **Properties**

The main Settings app lets you tweak your computer, smartphone, or tablet. But each individual app also has its own Settings menu with more customization options. Use this menu to change how the app displays notifications, the look of an app, and more.

To access these settings, open an app, then click or tap its menu button. On mobile devices, this usually appears as three dots or three lines. Depending on your device, it may be in the top left-hand or right-hand corner. Select the *Settings* option.

Experiment without fear

Settings are a great way to understand how to customize your tech devices. If you can become confident at changing and using settings, you'll be well on your way to mastering your computer, smartphone, or tablet.

One of the best ways to get better with the Settings app is to simply experiment. Change settings and see what happens. It's difficult to do any real damage, and most devices will warn you with a pop-up box if you are changing something major.

If you see a warning box and are not sure what you are going to change, simply press the *Cancel* button.

Keep notes on everything you change in settings. You may think it will be easy to remember what you've done, but when you're navigating through menus and looking at dozens and dozens of options, you're likely to lose track. If you keep a notebook or log of these changes, you'll be able to retrace your steps and switch things back later if necessary.

6 no-sweat steps to an internet connection

Nearly 8 out of every 10 American adults go online at least once a day. If you count yourself among them, setting up your device's internet connection is one of your biggest priorities. Here's how to use your Settings app to add a Wi-Fi connection to your device.

1. On your phone, tablet, or computer, search for *Network & Internet* or *Connections* in your Settings app. You may also see a specific option for Wi-Fi.

2. Make sure the Wi-Fi button is set to the on position. This means that your device will actively seek out a signal to connect to.

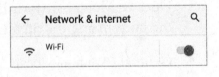

3. A list of available Wi-Fi networks will be displayed. If you are setting up your internet at home, this could be the name of your internet service provider. Or it could be the name of your router, which is the device that connects to the internet and transmits a Wi-Fi signal. Click or tap the name of the Wi-Fi network you want to join.

4. Enter the password. If you do not know your Wi-Fi password, it may be located on the body of your router.

5. Select the *Join* or *Connect* button to finalize the internet link.

6. Open a web browser on your device and go to any website to check that your connection is working.

Desktop computers and many laptops can also connect to the internet using a wired connection, known as Ethernet. To use a wired connection, simply run an Ethernet cable from your router to your computer. You won't need to enter a password to go online.

Check these out: 8 basic settings you can't ignore

The Settings menu is your doorway to the inner workings of your computer, smartphone, or tablet. Jump in and explore all the categories, options, and menus. No need to be afraid. Start off with these common settings.

- System (for Windows and Android). Change the settings for time, language, sound, display, notifications, and more.

- Dock & Menu bar (for Mac). Customize both the Dock at the bottom and the menu bar at the top of your Desktop.

- General (Apple devices). Access options for the overall appearance, date, time, and keyboard.

- Notifications. Specify how your alerts are handled. Change which apps can send notifications, how they appear, and what they look like.

- Accounts. View the details of the user accounts connected to a specific device. Add more accounts, such as email addresses, or add more users to a device.

- Search. Determine what can appear in the device's search results and manage voice-activated digital assistants. These include Cortana for Windows, Siri for Apple devices, and Google Assistant for Android devices.

- Battery. Display how much battery power is remaining for a mobile device or laptop, check which apps use the most battery power, and put the device into an energy-saving mode.

- Software updates. Check to see if there are new changes for the device's operating system. Make sure to regularly install updates to fix bugs and keep your device as secure as possible.

4 bright ideas give your device a makeover

Want to put your own personal stamp on your device — like tweaking the sounds, colors, and background? Go to Settings and check out these options.

- Personalization (Windows). Change the Desktop background, color settings, and overall theme for your computer. Customize the Lock screen, Start menu, and Taskbar.

- Display. Adjust the appearance and brightness of your device's screen. One option is Dark Mode, which shifts the screen so that windows and text boxes have a dark background and light text. This is good for extending your battery life or when using the device at night.

- Wallpaper. Choose a new background image for your Desktop or Home screen.

- Sound. Change the volume, decide which sounds play for alerts, turn silent mode on or off, and select sounds when you use the virtual keyboard on a tablet or smartphone.

Don't skip these privacy-protecting settings

Your devices are packed with sensitive financial information, personal photos, and more. If you ignore important security functions, you increase the risk of dangerous hackers and viruses. Look for these options in Settings under the security or privacy section.

- Enable the default antivirus app, if there is one installed. If you download different antivirus software, make it the default.

- Turn on the device's built-in firewall to prevent malicious software and viruses from getting into your computer through the internet.

- Set location services. Devices may use GPS, Wi-Fi, or other data to track your current location. Decide which apps you don't want accessing this information.

- Under App permissions, specify which ones can access other elements on your device. For example, some apps may want to use your camera or microphone. Unless it's necessary to record video or audio, don't allow this.

- Advertising options let you decide which ads your device will allow. It's best to keep these as limited as possible.

Ready, set, print — with this easy-to-follow guide

You can get so much more out of your computer if you know how to connect it to accessories. One of the most common devices to link to is a printer. Here's how to make sure you're set up and ready to print at home.

Windows. Want to add a printer to your Windows computer? Follow these simple steps.

1. Turn on the printer and connect it to your computer using the provided cable. This is usually a USB cable.

2. Open the Settings app on your computer. Click on *Bluetooth & devices*.

3. Select the *Printers & scanners* option.

4. Click on the *Add device* button.

5. Choose the printer from the list on the *Printers and scanners* menu. Click on the printer's name to view more details and set it as your default printer.

The printer should now be set up and ready to go. However, if you are having trouble making it work, you may need to update your driver. This is software that allows your computer to communicate with the printer. To see if you need a new driver, open the Start menu and go to Settings > Windows Update. Click *Check for updates*.

Mac. This quick guide can help you link your printer to a Mac.

1. Connect the printer to the Mac with the provided cable and make sure both devices are turned on.

2. Open System Settings on your Mac and select *Printers & Scanners*.

3. Click on this button to add a new printer.

4. Select a printer name from the list and click on the
    Add button.

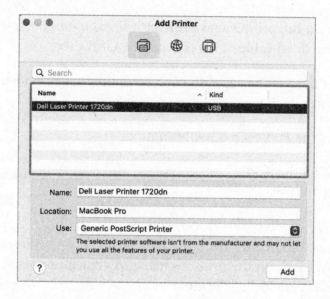

You should now see the device under the *Printers* list in the
Printers & Scanners window.

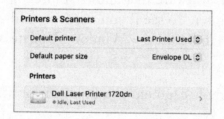

Forget the wires: Set up Bluetooth in a jiffy

Almost all modern computers and mobile devices let you use
Bluetooth-enabled accessories. This short-range wireless connection
is a great way to link to a computer mouse or keyboard without

untangling a mess of wires and cables. These simple steps will help you set up Bluetooth like a pro.

1. Turn on the accessory you want to connect to. In addition to a wireless mouse or keyboard, this could be a speaker, printer, headphones, or earbuds. In some cases you may need to turn the accessory's Bluetooth on.

2. Open the Settings app on your computer, smartphone, or tablet and tap or click on the *Bluetooth* option.

3. Make sure the Bluetooth button is switched to the on position. This lets your device search for a signal from Bluetooth-enabled accessories.

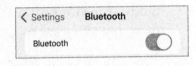

4. Select the *Add device* or *Pair new device* button.

5. Select the accessory you want to connect to.

6. Accept the request to pair or connect with the Bluetooth accessory.

11 Protection

The average American household has 11 tech devices, including smartphones, computers, and tablets. These cost a pretty penny, plus they're often home to your favorite photos, family videos, and important documents. That means if anything happens to them, not only could you lose hundreds — even thousands — of dollars' worth of equipment, but priceless memories, as well.

With a little know-how, though, you can protect your tech from damage, loss, or theft. Taking a few simple steps can guarantee that your devices and information will always be safe and sound.

Device defense — the 1 thing you must buy

Your tech devices spend much or all of their life plugged in to your main electrical supply. If there is a lightning strike, or something else that causes the voltage to spike, it can fry your pricey gadgets. The good news? A simple surge protector can give you peace of mind.

Also known as a surge or spike suppressor, it looks similar to an extension cord, and works by increasing the electrical resistance if it detects too much voltage coming through the line. That means anything plugged into it doesn't get suddenly overloaded. And you can relax knowing your devices are protected from catastrophic increases in electrical power. Buy surge protectors at hardware or electronic stores.

Don't let grime put your computer in danger

Dirt and dust on your computer isn't just unsightly — it's destructive. If you want your machine to last as long as possible, clean it regularly. Here are some of the most important areas to spiff up.

- Dust that builds up in and on the body of your computer can block airflow. That causes the device to retain more heat, which puts stress on the expensive components. To safely clean your computer, use a can of compressed air to blow out fine particles.

- A smudged screen may be a pain to look at, but don't use just anything to clean it off. Water will fry the electronics, and certain cloths can scratch the display. Wipe it regularly with a lint-free, microfiber cloth — similar to the type used to clean eyeglasses. You can also buy computer screen wipes specially designed for electronics.

- Keyboards are notorious for accumulating dust and crumbs. To clean yours, unplug it from your computer or power it off, then turn it upside down. Gently shake it to dislodge any debris. Compressed air will clean out anything that is still stuck in between the keys.

It's tempting to have a cup of coffee or glass of water nearby while you're typing, but be careful. All it takes is one spill to fry the sensitive electronics in your keyboard or computer. Drinking or eating near your devices is a bad idea.

4 wise ways to thwart tech thieves

Your tablets, laptops, and smartphones are attractive to thieves for two reasons. First, they are valuable electronics they can resell. And second, they're usually loaded with personal and financial information they can use to steal your identity. Fortunately, with a little preparation you can guard your devices against theft.

- Consider a home safe. This is a great way to keep your devices locked up and hidden when you're away from the house.

- Stash your devices in a large pocket or secure bag when traveling. If they are inconspicuous, you don't look like an easy mark for a snatch-and-grab robbery.

- Never lend tech devices to strangers. Someone may ask to borrow your phone to make a call or send a text, only to run away with it.

- Insure all your devices. You can purchase individual computer or phone coverage, but in many cases your home insurance covers electronics in the event of certain natural disasters or theft.

As soon as you get a new computer, tablet, or smartphone, ensure it's protected from viruses and other malware with good, reputable antivirus software.

Many devices come with default apps that guard against viruses, but you may want to consider choosing a third-party program for more protection. See Chapter 21 for details about using antivirus software.

Never lose your device with this simple hack

Smartphones and tablets are great when you're on the go. But this mobility comes with a major downside. These devices are much more likely to get lost or stolen. However, even if something disappears, don't panic.

The Find My function for tablets and smartphones can help you track down a device that's gone AWOL. It uses a GPS signal to pinpoint its last known location and displays this position on a map. You may also remotely lock your phone or tablet to prevent unauthorized access.

Log in to the iCloud website to track down lost Apple devices, or use your Google Account to search for a missing Android.

You can't track a missing phone or tablet unless you've first set up the Find My feature. So as soon as you get a new mobile device, turn this on. Normally this is done from the device's Settings app. If you're having trouble locating it, type "find my" into the Settings search bar.

Safeguard your files easy-peasy

A computer crash, broken phone, or stolen tablet is devastating. You could lose favorite photos, important files, and more. But just by creating regular backups, you can protect all your information. This involves making a copy of the data on your device and storing it in a safe location. That way, if anything happens, you'll have a duplicate ready to go. Here are two main ways to make a backup.

- External Storage. Buy an external hard drive or flash drive to house a copy of all your important files. Make sure to get one with more memory than your device's main drive so there's plenty of room for everything. Store this backup drive in a secure location separate from your computer, phone, or tablet.

- Online Cloud Services. These let you store all your data onto a remote server. You can access these files from anywhere you have internet, so no need to fret about losing track of a physical hard drive. Most major operating systems offer their own dedicated cloud service that can automatically back up the information from your device. For more information on using them, see Chapter 23.

Recapture lost data — even if you've trashed it

Every now and then, it's a good idea to go through and delete unwanted files and folders from your computer. This helps free up space on your hard drive and can keep your computer from getting bogged down. But sometimes you may accidentally throw something away or change your mind about keeping it. Don't worry — as long as you have not emptied your trash, it's not lost forever. Here's how to get it back.

On a Windows computer.

1. Double-click on the Recycle Bin icon on your Desktop.

2. Find the file you don't want deleted and single-click on it.

3. Click on the *Restore the selected items* button in the top toolbar. This will return the file to its original location.

If you want to save everything in the Recycle Bin, click on the *Restore all items* button.

On a Mac.

1. Click on the Trash icon in your Dock.

2. Select the file you want to restore by clicking on it. Then right-click or press Ctrl on your keyboard and click to open the Options menu.

3. Select *Put Back* to restore the item to its original location.

If you want to simply move an item out of the Trash, click, hold, and drag it from the Trash window onto your Desktop.

When you choose *Empty Recycle Bin* on a Windows machine or *Empty Trash* on a Mac, be aware this permanently deletes the contents. Make sure there isn't anything you want to save before taking this action.

12 Maintenance

Tech isn't cheap. You can easily spend hundreds — even thousands — of dollars on electronics. The last thing your wallet needs is for you to have to replace or upgrade a device after only a year or two.

The good news — with just a little know-how you can take steps to extend the life span of your devices. Read on to find tips and tricks that will make sure your phones, tablets, and computers will still work for longer than you thought possible.

5 tasks help your tech run for years

Want your electronics to stay in tiptop shape? These regular housekeeping tasks can help extend the life expectancy of your devices. And as an added bonus, doing these every month may make your computer, phone, or tablet run a bit faster, too.

Clean out your storage. Is your device loaded with unwanted photos, apps you don't use, and more? Go through it occasionally and delete old files to clean up space.

Empty your virtual Trash or Recycle Bin. When you delete items, they aren't, in fact, actually removed. Instead, they're saved here until you permanently delete them. So if you go too long without emptying your trash, it can get extremely full. This can slow down your hard drive and clutter your computer.

Defragment your hard drive. This reorganizes data so that all the pieces of a file are in the same location, which makes your device work more efficiently. On a Windows computer, use the Defragment and Optimize Drives app. Download specific apps for defragmenting a Mac computer from the App Store.

Set up a screen saver or auto lock. This will put your device to sleep after it's been sitting unused for a while. Doing so saves power and extends the life of your electronics. You'll find ways to enable these in Settings.

Turn off your device. If you're not going to use a piece of tech, turn it off completely. And even if you use a device every day, turning it off every so often gives it the chance to perform updates.

Weather watch: Extreme temp survival guide

Most electronics don't hold up well when exposed to the elements. While you know to keep your computer out of the rain, you may be surprised to learn just how dangerous extreme temperatures can be.

- Avoid leaving your electronics in direct sunlight or in a parked car on a warm day. The delicate circuitry will overheat. If you do have to leave a phone or tablet in a sunny spot, turn it off and store it in an insulated case.

- Extremely cold temperatures can damage the battery and other components. Keep your devices warm or in insulated bags if they're going to be somewhere very cold for an extended period of time. If you do leave something out in the cold, let it warm up to room temperature for a few hours before turning it on.

Keep your devices high and dry

Water and electricity don't mix well. Even though many smartphones and other tech devices are advertised as water-resistant, don't take a chance.

- While it may be tempting to use your laptop when lounging at the pool, even a little splash could fry your machine. Some smartphones or tablets may hold up better to a bit of moisture, but avoid submerging them for any length of time.

- Consider keeping your tech in a waterproof bag if there's a chance of rain. Frequent travelers may want a robust case from an outdoor supply store, but a plastic zip-close bag can work in a pinch.

If your device does get soaked, dry it out completely before you turn it on again or risk damaging the electronics inside. Cover it in uncooked rice or silica gel for a day or two to help draw out the water.

If you're giving away or selling your device, make sure there's no personal data left on it. To do this, return the device to its original factory settings. Open the Settings app and search for "Reset." Find the option to erase all content and settings.

Give old electronics a second life

Despite your best efforts, tech devices will reach the end of the road eventually. But don't simply throw them away.

Sell. While your device may be too damaged or old for you, there may be someone out there who can make use of it. Websites like eBay are a great way to earn money for old electronics. Other sites, like *wireflytradeins.cexchange.com* let you trade them in for cash.

Donate. Charities or churches often repurpose old computers, smartphones, or other devices.

Recycle. Many companies offer free recycling for old tech. Check with your local electronics store to see if they'll take yours.

Make your smartphone battery last all day

Poor battery life on your smartphone is frustrating. You want to make calls, take pictures, or more without having to top up the charge every few hours. And running low isn't just stressful — it's bad for your battery's life span.

When the charge drops below 20%, it puts excess strain on the battery and causes it to wear out faster. These five simple tricks will help you get a bit more juice out of your device.

- Put your phone in Low Power Mode. This disables certain settings and automatic functions so you use less energy. To turn it on, go to the Settings app and tap on *Battery*.

- Turn down your screen brightness. Your phone's display draws a considerable amount of power. Also try turning on Dark mode, so the background is black and text is white.

- Don't let your phone run all day. Open your Settings app and search for Auto lock. Here you control how quickly your phone turns the display off or goes into Sleep mode. Select the shortest amount of time possible.

- Turn off Wi-Fi and Bluetooth if you're not using them. Otherwise, your phone is constantly burning energy to seek out internet or Bluetooth signals.

- Turn off Location Services. Some apps continually check your location using cell signal or GPS. This is great if you need directions or want up-to-date weather info, but it uses a lot of power. Go to the Settings app to turn this off or limit which apps can access your location.

Want to charge your phone on the go? Consider getting a portable battery bank. These devices store power so you can charge your electronics when you're nowhere near an outlet.

13 Accessibility

Computers, smartphones, and tablets are a mainstay of everyday life. That means tech companies must ensure as many people as possible are able to use their devices. For those with limited vision, hearing problems, or impaired motor skills, it can be tough to master many electronics right out of the box.

Thankfully, most have Accessibility settings that can make devices easy for anybody to use. Read on to discover how to enlarge text, change your screen setup so it's easier to navigate, and more.

Discover hidden features you'll want to use

Having trouble reading the text on your screen? Maybe you need colorblind filters for an easier time navigating the icons on your smartphone. Or perhaps you don't even know all the different things you can change to make your device easier to use.

Start by opening your Settings app. Click or tap on the *Accessibility* menu and browse through all the categories.

If you need more Accessibility features than your device offers, consider downloading specialized apps. Go to the App Store on Apple devices, the Microsoft Store on Windows computers, or the Google Play Store on Android devices. Type "accessibility" into the search box and take your pick from the displayed options.

3 smart settings relieve eyestrain

Instead of squinting to read tiny text on your smartphone, laptop, or computer, use these visual Accessibility options to give your peepers a break.

Text size. If all the words everywhere on your device are too small to read, don't worry. Simply change the default font size.

1. Open your Settings app and select *Accessibility*.

2. Select *Text size* or *Font size*.

3. Use the slider to make the text larger or smaller. A preview will display the new default text size.

4. Click or tap on the *Apply* button to set the new text size. On some devices the change is applied automatically.

Magnification. Use this feature to increase the size of a specific area of your screen — as if you're looking at it under a magnifying glass. This can help you focus on a small part of a window without having to make all the text and icons larger.

1. Open your Settings app and select *Accessibility*.

2. Turn the *Zoom*, *Magnifier*, or *Magnification* option to the on position.

3. On some devices, a box that magnifies everything inside it will appear on your screen. Other devices may simply let you zoom in by tapping the screen or pressing certain buttons.

4. Move the box around the screen or press your screen and swipe to change the area that is magnified.

Some devices may have a toolbar that will let you change certain settings, such as the level of magnification. If you don't see a toolbar, use the Settings app to adjust it. Also, be aware that you can't select apps or text on your screen that aren't currently inside the Magnifier box.

Narration. Depending on your device, this may be known as a screen reader, a narrator, or text-to-speech setting. An Apple product may call it VoiceOver.

In a nutshell, this setting plays an audio version of the text on your screen, which makes it great for people with visual impairments. Here's generally how to turn it on and use it.

1. Open your Settings app and select *Accessibility*.

2. Find *VoiceOver, Narration,* or *Text-to-speech output.* Toggle this option to the on position.

3. Adjust the tone of the voice and how quickly it reads back text.

4. Click or tap an item on your screen to listen to the narrator read it out loud. As the narrator advances, the text being read is highlighted on your screen.

If you don't like the default narration settings, or if your device doesn't have a text-to-speech option, you can download narration apps from your device's app store.

Using the narration feature may slightly change the swipes, taps, or clicks that you normally use to navigate your device, so it may take some practice to get used to it.

Turn on alerts for important household sounds

If you're hard of hearing, you might miss the doorbell or, tragically, a smoke alarm. Some devices though — like smartphones and tablets — have settings that turn on alerts when they detect certain sounds.

Android tablets and phones.

1. Open your device's Settings app.

2. Tap Accessibility > Sound Notifications and select *Open Sound Notifications*.

3. Tap *OK* to accept permissions and enable your device to start listening.

Add sounds to listen for in the Settings app by going to Accessibility > Sound Notifications. Tap *Open Sound Notifications* and select *Settings*. Tap *Sound Notifications are active*. Choose which sounds you want your phone to listen for. You can turn on notifications that alert you when the doorbell rings, if your device detects the sound of running water, and more.

Apple tablets and phones.

1. Open the Settings app.

2. Tap on Accessibility > Sound Recognition, then toggle the *Sound Recognition* button to the on position.

3. Choose which sounds you want your phone or tablet to listen for.

Don't see a sound you want to add? Go to Settings > Accessibility > Sound Recognition > Sounds and tap *Custom Alarm* or *Custom Appliance* or *Doorbell*. Place your phone or tablet near the source of the sound, and select *Start Listening* to add the sound. Follow the on-screen instructions to finish the setup.

Never miss a notification with this surefire trick

Smartphones and tablets use chimes and dings to let you know when you have a text, call, alarm, or other notification. But if your hearing isn't great, it's easy to miss these alerts.

You can always turn them on vibrate, but that doesn't do much if you don't have the device in your pocket. So if you want a can't-miss signal, turn on LED or Flash notifications. These cause your device's light or screen to flash on and off in order to get your attention.

Android tablets and phones.

1. Open the Settings app and select *Accessibility*.

2. Go to the Hearing category.

3. Find the *Flash Alerts* button and toggle it to the on position.

On certain Android devices, the *Flash Alerts* button may be under a different menu. Use the search bar in your Settings app to track it down if you're having trouble finding it.

Apple tablets and phones.

1. Open the Settings app and tap on *Accessibility*.

2. Scroll down to the Hearing category and tap on *Audio/Visual*.

3. Tap on *LED Flash for Alerts*. Change the button to the on position.

Most new smartphones are hearing aid compatible (HAC), which means they connect with hearing aids to boost and clarify your phone conversations.

Some hearing aids can also pair with certain phone apps so you can hear alerts or operate your hearing aid with help from your phone. Ask about these features when shopping for a new hearing aid.

If you have mild or moderate hearing loss, consider taking advantage of over-the-counter options. A new FDA rule allowing hearing aids to be sold directly to consumers in stores or online without a medical exam or a fitting by an audiologist means it's never been cheaper to get one. You'll need to fit and adjust it yourself, so opt for one with a user-friendly app and smartphone compatibility.

If you have severe hearing loss, however, let a trained hearing health professional determine which device is right for you.

Turn audio into text with 1 setting

Captions and subtitles are excellent for watching movies or TV shows if you have trouble hearing. But that's not all they're great for. Some apps also provide real-time captions for video calls, letting you follow along without cranking up the volume. Here's how to turn them on.

1. Open your Settings app and select *Accessibility*.

2. Find the Hearing category and select *Captions* or *Subtitles*. The exact menu name may be slightly different depending on the device you are using.

3. Toggle the *Captions* or *Subtitles* option to the on position.

4. You'll see a preview of the text style. Select *Options* to make changes to the size and style of the captions.

Clear-cut viewing: How to fine-tune your display

Changing the default colors on your device's screen could make it easier to read and understand text or help you see icons more clearly if you're colorblind. Open the Settings app and select *Accessibility*. Then experiment with these two display options.

- Color filters. These can change the overall color theme on your device, including the background on which text is displayed. Tinker with a few options to see if any make your device easier to use.

- Contrast. Enhance the difference between main elements on your screen and make certain menu selections easier to see. You can invert colors or use default backgrounds so text is more distinct.

Depending on the device, you may turn off menu options and icons that rely solely on color, reduce the intensity of certain bright colors, and change button color indicators to labels so you know when they are *On* or *Off*.

Hands down — best relief for hand pain

Tech devices can be tricky to use if you have a limited range of motion in your hands. The good news? With the right accessibility features, it's possible to set up your phone, tablet, or computer to work with you instead of against you.

Touch screen tweaks. Do your hands hurt while attempting those intricate taps, swipes, and gestures required on touch screens? Are tiny devices difficult to navigate? Experiment with these options.

- Turn on Reachability or One-handed mode so you don't need to use both hands to navigate larger touch screens.

- Use built-in voice controls or digital assistants to open apps, search for items, and more without having to touch or type.

- Connect a keyboard or touchpad to your phone or tablet so you can select apps, type, and more without using the touch screen.

The exact menu names and options vary depending on which device you are using. Explore the Accessibility menu to see more options.

Keyboard and mouse adjustments. While on your computer, you may find it tough to use the default keyboard and mouse. Try changing these settings.

- Adjust the sensitivity of the keys on your keyboard. Some models allow you to change it so they require more — or less — pressure to activate a key.

- Turn on a virtual, on-screen keyboard if you have trouble typing on a physical one.

- Play sounds that let you know which key you press while typing.

- Move your mouse cursor around the screen by pressing the number pad on your keyboard.

Specially designed keyboards and computer mice have ergonomic features and color-coded buttons that make them easy to use. Ask about these options at your local electronics store.

14 Printers and printing

Printers became a home office staple almost as soon as personal computers made an appearance. However, these days you may find you're printing less and less. It's easy to fill out paperwork online and share documents via email.

So the hundred dollar question is, do you still need a printer? Many people may head to the library or office supply store on the rare occasion they want a paper document. But if you prefer the convenience of a home printer or must print a lot at home, there are plenty of good quality, inexpensive printers on the market.

Pick the perfect printer

When shopping for a new printer, the first decision is whether you want to go inkjet or laser. How do you know which is best for you? Check out some pros and cons for each.

- Inkjet printers tend to have lower upfront costs. They're great at printing colorful pictures and documents. However, the ink cartridges for these are more expensive than the ones used for laser printers, and the ink can dry up over time.

- Laser printers are perfect for handling black and white documents, especially text-heavy pages. They're more expensive, but they produce sharper text and print faster than most inkjets.

The fine print: 2 ways to connect

A printer can't do anything unless it's hooked up to a computer or another device. Here are two of the main ways to connect and get ready to print.

- Wired. Most printers come with a cable that can plug directly into a computer. This is the easiest way to set up and connect most devices. The downside is you'll only be able to print while your computer is physically connected to the printer.

- Wireless. Most, but not all, modern printers can connect to devices without a physical cord. They may use Wi-Fi or Bluetooth. If your printer has this option, you can put it almost anywhere in your house. You can also connect your phone or tablet this way and print from them.

See Chapter 10 for more details about setting up a printer and connecting it to a computer.

Don't want to drive from store to store looking at printer prices? After you've decided what you want to buy, use price comparison websites to find the best deal. Check out *shopsavvy.com*, *price-grabber.com*, and *shopping.com*.

Page setup simplified

Want to become a printing pro? With a little know-how, you can tweak your printer's options to optimize speed, quality, and ink savings. These will vary slightly depending on your printer, your computer, and which app you're printing from.

1. Select *Print Preview* or *Print* in the menu bar on your computer, smartphone, or tablet.

2. The Print window will show different setup options. To view more, click on the *Properties* button.

3. Select which pages you want to print and the number of copies you want.

4. Select the orientation for the printed document — Portrait or Landscape.

5. Choose which paper size you want to print on. Make sure you choose the size that matches the paper in your printer.

6. Decide if you want to print on one side of the paper or both. Some printers will not automatically print double-sided.

7. Choose your print quality. Higher quality will take longer and use more ink, but have more detail. This is a good option if you're printing photographs or legal documents.

Once all of your print options are set up properly, click or tap the *Print* or *OK* button.

3 steps to preserve your precious ink

Ounce for ounce, printer ink is one of the most expensive items in the tech world. In fact, some of the priciest printer inks cost upwards of $9,500 a gallon. While you only use a tiny bit each time you print, it just makes sense to use your ink wisely. Try these pointers to save ink — and money.

*   Use the lowest quality print setting you can get away with. This means you'll use less ink and your printer will work faster.

*   Look for third-party ink cartridges. These often work just as well without costing an arm and a leg.

- Do regular maintenance on your printer. Old, dried-out ink can build up and cause poor quality prints and wasted ink. Many printers have a cleaning or maintenance cycle. Run it frequently to keep your printer at peak performance.

Do you make the common mistake of changing your printer's cartridge every time a low ink level warning light comes on? Most of the time, there's a considerable amount of ink left in there. Some even estimate that the cartridge is still 40% full. Before replacing it with an expensive, new cartridge, keep using the cartridges in your printer until the quality becomes unacceptable.

Forget the scanner — try these free apps instead

Need to scan a document? If you don't have a scanner and there isn't one built in to your printer, don't go out and buy another device. You can use your smartphone's camera and free apps to quickly scan items. Use your device's app store to search for these.

- Adobe Scan
- CamScanner
- Genius Scan

Don't toss away your store receipts too quickly. They may have QR codes or barcodes that can be scanned and converted into rewards points or coupons at certain stores. Dedicated apps, like Ibotta and Receipt Hog, can help you track these offers and redeem them at participating stores.

Top 10 Tips for Your Devices

1. Spend some time becoming familiar with the settings options on your electronics so you can take advantage of all the features.

2. Don't be afraid to adjust the settings on your devices. Just make sure to keep a note of everything you modify, in case you change your mind.

3. Back up the content on your devices regularly so you never lose important digital documents, videos, or photos.

4. A surge protector is a cheap and effective way to safeguard your electronics if there is a power spike.

5. Extreme temperatures and water don't mix well with most tech devices. Do your best to keep your expensive electronics safe from the elements.

6. A portable power bank can charge your phone, tablet, or other device while you're on the go.

7. Recycling old electronics is great for the planet and could even put a bit of extra cash in your pocket.

8. Certain accessibility settings, such as changing the default text size on your screen, could make your tech devices a lot easier to use.

9. Captions or subtitles are a brilliant way to enjoy movies, videos, or video calls without worrying about the volume.

10. Consider your printer needs carefully before buying one. You may find that an inkjet printer makes more sense than a laser printer, or that you don't need a printer at all.

Digital Security

Chapter 15 Banking

The internet has changed the way almost every company does business — and banks are no exception. Over the years, they've added more and more online features. Now, you can use your computer or smartphone to check your account balance, transfer funds, and even deposit checks. If you want to make managing your money easier and safer, learn how to navigate online banking.

Put your money where your mouse is

As long as you have an internet connection, it's easy to access your bank account online to transfer funds and more. However, before you can start, you'll need to set everything up. Follow this guide to do it quickly and safely.

1. From your secure home computer, go to your bank's website.

2. Find the *New Account* section. If you're not sure where this is, check to see if the website has a search box or customer service section that can help you locate it.

3. To set up the new account, you'll need to give them an email address and create a username and password. If you already have a physical account with the bank, you will need some extra verification to finalize the setup. This may involve proof of address, your Social Security number, or other information.

Once you have all your account information, you can access your online account from the web or using a mobile app you download to your phone or tablet. Make sure to keep your account password and username safe and secure.

Most traditional brick-and-mortar banks offer services online. But there are also online-only banks, which don't have any physical branches.

One of the advantages of these is that they generally offer lower fees and higher interest rates than mainstream banks. That's partly because they don't have the expense of building maintenance. You could save up to $160 a year by moving your money to this kind of bank.

If you're interested in trying out an online-only bank, choose one that's properly regulated. Here are a few to check out.

- Alliant Credit Union at *alliantcreditunion.org*

- Ally at *ally.com*

- Axos Bank at *axosbank.com*

- Discover Bank at *discover.com*

- Varo at *varomoney.com*

Plug online security holes to protect your cash

When you walk into an actual bank, you know your personal information is being handled safely. But when all it takes is a smartphone or computer to access your account, it may seem less secure.

It's true, hackers and scammers use high-tech tactics to try and get money from your account. The good news? With a little know-how you can make sure your hard-earned dollars are protected even if you choose to bank online.

Keep your login details private. Never give out your account number, username, or password to anyone.

Don't use dodgy networks. You wouldn't say your PIN out loud at the ATM, would you? But when you log in to your bank account on a public Wi-Fi, you're broadcasting your password to hackers.

Keep an eye out for fishy emails. If you get an official looking notice about password changes you don't remember making or attempts to access your account, stop. It could either be a scheme to compromise your info or a sign it's already happened. Don't click on any of the links in these emails. But do contact your bank directly to make sure your money is safe.

Check your accounts regularly. Suspicious activity could be a sign that someone has stolen your info. If you catch it early enough, your bank can help you get back your money. Work with your bank to turn on automatic text or email alerts for whenever you make a purchase. That way you can know when someone else initiates a transaction on your account.

Don't panic. This is particularly true if you are contacted and asked for any of your bank details. It could be a fraudster trying to get you to divulge sensitive information about your online banking activities. In many cases, these scams operate by pressuring people into thinking they have to make a quick decision to stop something bad happening to their account. If in doubt, ask for more time to think about it.

Notify authorities of potential scams. Contact your bank if you think you've been approached by a scammer. If you're not sure a call or email is legitimate, call your bank directly and tell them the details. If it was a genuine email or call they will be able to verify it.

Check your bank's policy on fraud. Make sure your financial institution has a guarantee against any fraud you may be a victim of as a result of online banking. Read this guarantee carefully.

You'll want to know the circumstances in which you will receive a full refund if you are a victim of an online fraud. In most cases you should get back 100% of your money, but check for any situations in which you would be liable for some of the costs. Details should be on the bank's website.

You might think you'll be safe from identity thieves if you stay off the internet. But that couldn't be further from the truth. If you're not online, you actually have a greater risk of becoming a victim.

That's because everyone from your bank to your utility company to the IRS uses online accounts. And if you don't create accounts for yourself, you leave them wide open for a bad guy to come in and do it on your behalf.

Quick and safe: Try a new way to pay

Out shopping? You may notice that more and more merchants are offering contactless payment options. Not only is this new feature quicker and more sanitary, it's more secure.

Contactless credit cards. Instead of swiping or inserting your credit card, all you have to do is hold your credit card near the reader until it emits a sound to let you know the payment is complete. Check with your bank to see if your credit card is compatible with contactless payment, or if you can get a card that is.

Apple Pay. Don't have a compatible card? Don't worry. You can still use contactless payments if you have a smartphone. Apple Pay, available on your iPhone and Apple Watch, lets you store card information — but not the actual card number — on your devices. When you want to use that card to make a payment, your passcode or FaceID authorizes the transaction. Follow these steps to set it up.

1. Open the Wallet app.

2. Press the + button in the top, right-hand corner and tap *Debit or Credit Card*.

Add to Wallet

Keep all the cards, keys, and passes you use every day all in one place.

Available Cards

	Apply for Apple Card	>
	Add Apple Account	>
	Debit or Credit Card	>
	Transit Card	>
	Driver's License or State ID	>

3. Add the details of your card. Once this is done, you will get a text or phone call to verify the card.

When you want to use your phone or watch to pay, simply open the Wallet app and choose which card you want to use. Hold the device close to the register and wait until you get confirmation that the payment went through.

Google Pay (G Pay). Android has its own virtual wallet you can use to pay via your phone. If the Google Wallet app is not already installed, download it from the Google Play Store.

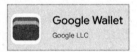

Google Wallet
Google LLC

Here's how to add cards to this virtual wallet.

1. Open the Google Wallet app.

2. Tap *Add to Wallet* at the bottom of the screen.

3. Tap *Payment card*.

4. Tap *New credit or debit card*. You can enter the details manually or use your camera to scan the card.

5. At the bottom, tap *Save*.

You may need to accept the terms of use and verify the card before it can be added to your phone.

2 times you should never use a debit card

When you don't want to carry around cash, a debit card may be just the ticket. Unlike credit cards, they are tied directly to your bank account balance, so you can never rack up debt. However, debit cards aren't nearly as safe online as credit cards.

- Never connect to public Wi-Fi then use your debit card to shop or pay bills. Fraudsters can easily lift your card details.

- Never use your debit card to shop online if the website doesn't have a padlock icon or "https" in the address bar. This indicates the site isn't secure.

Don't swipe your debit card at independent ATMs. Not only can your bank charge you a fee if the ATM is not in your network, but these are prime locations for thieves to hide card skimmers. Once you use your debit card and punch in the PIN, scammers could have access to all the cash in your account.

16 Passwords

Modern technology means you can bank online, shop with the click of a button, and share photos with friends and family members across the globe. However, you still need to keep all your personal and financial details safe. Otherwise, anybody could pretend to be you or access your money.

That's where passwords come in — vital tools that lock down your online accounts. But they can be tricky, right? After all, it's difficult to keep track of dozens of passwords, remember to update them regularly, and make sure they're strong enough to deter hackers. Start today transforming your online passwords from a digital annoyance into powerful protection.

Create a hack-proof password

Hackers can write programs that guess thousands — even millions — of passwords in mere minutes. So if you really want to create a password that could take over 4 centuries to guess, you'll need to follow this advice.

Make your passwords long. The more characters a password has, the harder it is for thieves to guess it. Experts say your passwords should be at least 12 characters, but longer is better.

Mix it up. A good password should have a combination of uppercase and lowercase letters, numbers, and symbols. One example of a tough-to-hack password would be something like "ckmyT3k$kM?dqPE4."

Avoid common combos. Simple passwords may be easy to remember, but they're also easy to crack. Amazingly, two of the most common passwords in use are "123456" and "PASSWORD," so they're often the first hackers will try.

Steer clear of personal details. Names of pets, birthdays, the numbers of your street address, and the names of children may seem like private details, but they're easier to guess than you think.

Make them unique. One password per account. If you reuse the same password over and over again, it only takes one security breach to compromise all of your online info. But if you use something different for every account, you're still protected if thieves manage to hack one of your passwords.

3 tips save you from password overload

If you can't remember which password goes to what account, you may be constantly resetting them — a time-consuming and often frustrating task.

Here are a few tips to help you keep track of this vital information.

- Use a password manager. These apps make sure you always have your info on hand.

- Store a physical copy of your passwords safely. Not only does this give you an easy way to reference your info, but you can share it with your loved ones if they need to log in to your accounts on your behalf. Just be sure to keep this printout in a secure location, such as a home safe. You don't want anyone having access to your bank accounts, email, or other info.

- Add a good password hint. Most websites and online accounts let you create a hint to jog your memory if you forget your password.

Never forget a password again

You love them — you hate them. No doubt, passwords protect you online, but they can be endlessly annoying to keep straight and secure. That's where a good password manager app comes in.

This software application stores your passwords and other login details for various accounts in an encrypted format, then automatically enters the information when you connect to a website. All you need is one master password to engage the manager.

Let an app help with common password headaches.

Store them safely. A password manager can save login info for dozens — even hundreds — of different accounts. Everything is coded and captured either on your device or in the app's designated cloud storage.

Power them up. Weak passwords invite hackers to break into your online accounts. But a password manager can generate ones that are secure, unique, and difficult to crack.

Make them distinct. It's important to use different passwords for different accounts. That way, if one is compromised thieves can't log in to other websites. These apps can check for duplicates and make sure you're not using the same one over and over again.

Switch them out. You need to change your passwords on a regular basis. This could be a lot of work, but password managers make it easy by alerting you when it's time to update.

There are many kinds of password managers with different types of encryption, storage, and additional features. Ready to find one? Check these out.

- *1password.com*

- *dashlane.com*

- *keepass.info*

- *lastpass.com*

- *roboform.com*

Use your device's app store to discover more password manager apps. Add one to your computer, smartphone, and tablet. But if you have a password manager on more than one device, use the same company for them all. That way you can sync account information across your electronics.

6 secrets to maximize your manager

Take advantage of all the features your password manager has to offer. These will fortify your defenses against hackers.

- Install the browser extension for your chosen manager onto your web browser. This makes using the app easy and automatic.

- Choose a strong password to sign securely into your password manager app, and keep it in a secure place. Some apps may allow you to use your computer's passcode, fingerprint scan, or facial recognition to sign in.

- There is a section in the app where you can go in and look at your passwords and other account information. Some may even warn you if you use the same password for different accounts.

- If possible, have your manager run an audit occasionally to scan for data breaches. If a password has been compromised, create a new, more secure one immediately.

- Allow your password manager to suggest a secure password. The best part? You don't even need to remember it. The app will automatically fill it in next time you want to connect to that account.

- Sync your info across devices. You may use both your home computer and your phone to log in to your online accounts. Some password managers let you share passwords and settings with multiple electronics.

Many password managers have a free and a paid version. Some features may only be available if you pay to upgrade.

iCloud Keychain: Secure and convenient

Apple devices — such as Mac computers, iPhones, and iPads — have a built-in feature that can create and securely store passwords. It's called Keychain.

To access it, open your Settings app and see if Keychain is enabled. If it is, you can store all of your passwords and share them across any device linked to the same iCloud account.

Double down on security with two-factor authentication

Want to add an extra layer of security to your online accounts? Use two-factor authentication. This feature asks you to provide further verification after entering your username and password to an online account. It could involve any of several strategies.

- asking you to use your phone to scan your fingerprint or face

- sending you an email or text message with a one-time use code that expires within a certain amount of time

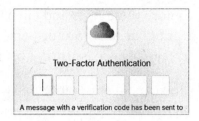

- using a dedicated two-factor authentication app

The bottom line is that nobody can access your accounts unless they also have your smartphone, tablet, or home computer.

Most websites allow you to enable this security feature when you want to log in. To turn it on, go to the websites' Account, Privacy, or Security settings and search for "Two-Factor Authentication." Make sure it is enabled, and choose a method of verification. You will likely need to provide a phone number or email address.

To fully protect your bank account, emails, and more, experts recommend you change your passwords at least once every year. This can help make sure your accounts are secure. However, if you think your accounts have been compromised, or if you know you've been the victim of a data breach, don't wait to change your login details. Create a new, secure password straight away.

Say scram to new scams

Scammers and hackers never seem to rest. They're constantly coming up with new ways of conning people out of their personal details.

Here's a new one to watch out for. You get a text or email that says your password is set to expire. All you have to do is click the link, enter your old password, and create a new one. The only problem? You've just handed over all your login info to a thief.

Ignore these texts and emails. Never reply to any communication with your password or personal details. Whenever you need to create a new password, go straight to the account's website or app.

To keep up with more password and tech-related scams, stay tuned in to tech news. It's a good idea to regularly check the list of common scams kept by the FBI. Go online to *fbi.gov/scams-and-safety/common-scams-and-crimes*.

Pilfered password? 5 things to do now

You did your best to protect your online information, but hackers breached a company website or database, and now they have a virtual key to your account. Take these steps immediately.

1. Change your password. Go straight to the compromised website and create a new, strong password. For good measure, do the same for all accounts that contain financial or personal information.

2. Turn on two-factor authentication, if you're not already using it. This gives you an added layer of protection.

3. Keep your eyes peeled for updates from the company. They may need a few days to find out who had their info stolen. Once they do, they should send out status reports and steps you can take to further protect yourself.

4. Watch out for suspicious activity. Thieves may attempt to access bank accounts or open new credit cards in your name if they have your info. Contact all financial institutions you deal with and put fraud alerts in place.

5. If your bank password or financial information was compromised, consider freezing your credit.

For other steps you can take to protect yourself, see Chapter 17.

17 Fraud and ID theft

Experts estimate that 1 out of 3 Americans face some form of identity theft at least once during their lives. This crime, which involves fraudsters stealing personal details for financial gain, costs billions of dollars every year. Thieves may open credit cards in your name, use your bank accounts to make unauthorized purchases, file fake tax returns to steal your refund, or even sell your info to other scammers.

And unfortunately, this crime is becoming more and more common. A few reasons why? Social media users may share too much of their personal information online, hackers can access public info from people using unsecured internet connections, and large online data breaches may compromise Social Security numbers or credit card info.

But with the right knowledge and preparation, you can safeguard your personal information from scammers and even recover from identity theft.

Stolen identity? Be alert for these 7 warning signs

ID theft can wreak havoc on your finances, credit, and personal life. One way to fight back against fraudsters is to learn to recognize these red flags.

- Unfamiliar charges on your bank or credit card statements.
- Checks that unexpectedly bounce due to insufficient funds.

- Unexplained drops in your credit score.

- Declined loans or credit card applications that you should qualify for.

- Changes to your medical files or mysterious medical bills.

- Unusual activity on your social media profile.

- Difficulty logging in to online accounts.

If you notice any of these signs, inform your bank and other appropriate companies about the fraudulent action as soon as possible.

Pre-approved credit card offers that show up in your box aren't just annoying junk mail. Each one puts you at risk of identity theft. If stolen by a scam artist, it can be used to open up a new credit card in your name.

But all it takes is one short phone call to put an end to these credit card offers and stop thieves from using them to steal your identity.

Simply dial 1-888-5-OPT-OUT (1-888-567-8688) or go online to *optoutprescreen.com*. You will have to give them your name, address, Social Security number, and date of birth.

Saving private info: Bright ideas for data defense

Identity thieves want to get as much information about you as they possibly can. Why? The more they know, the easier it is for them to impersonate you. Here are some of the common things they'll try to get their hands on.

- name
- Social Security number

- address
- birthdate

- driver's license number
- bank statements
- debit and credit card numbers
- utility bills
- login details for online accounts

You might be surprised by what unscrupulous people will do to gain this information. Take these steps to protect your privacy.

Watch what you post on social media. These websites are a gold mine of personal info. Con artists will create fake profiles and use the details you provide to connect with you online. If you give them access — by "friending" them, for instance — they can poke around your account looking for material to exploit. One tactic is to search your photos for any sensitive information lurking in the background, such as a snippet of your bank account number or an address.

Restrict who has your personal info. Thieves may send you emails, text messages, or even approach you in person to obtain private details. Don't give out any of your information to someone you can't trust completely.

Keep personal documents safe. Store any important paperwork in a secure place, such as a home lock box or a safe deposit box. If you are going to be away from home for a while, ask a friend to collect your mail and keep it confidential, too.

Shred old paperwork. You may throw out bills and credit card statements without a second thought. But fraudsters are known to dig through trash to find these nuggets of personal information. Before you put them in the bin, shred all documents containing your name, address, phone numbers, email addresses, driver's license number, Social Security number, passwords, or PINs. In addition, shred the following.

- address labels from junk mail and magazines
- bank statements
- credit reports
- investment documents
- pre-approved credit card applications
- canceled and voided checks
- expired credit cards
- employee pay stubs

- insurance information
- ATM receipts
- travel itineraries
- medical and dental records
- tax forms
- used airline tickets

Protect yourself from this surprising source of fraud

Don't think that guarding against strangers is all it takes to avoid identity theft and scams. Some crooks are much closer to home than you suspect.

Shady relations. It may not be a slick, professional con artist who cheats you out of your money. For many seniors, financial swindles come from their own unscrupulous children, grandchildren, nieces, nephews, brothers, or sisters. Be suspicious if a relative you've trusted to handle your finances keeps you from checking your accounts.

Gullible kinfolk. Even if your family members aren't trying to steal your info, they can still compromise your security. Some scammers will reach out and ask them seemingly innocent questions, like "Could you let me know your sister's birthday so I can send her a card?" Or "When will your grandmother be on vacation?"

While it may seem like no big deal, this could be all it takes to jeopardize your identity. Speak to your closest relatives about fraud and make sure no one shares any personal information without your approval.

Fake family. Some scammers call and claim to be a relative in an attempt to trick you out of money or personal details.

A common con is the grandparent scam. An impostor will call, claiming to be your grandchild. He says he's been arrested and needs you to immediately wire money to post bail. Crying, he begs you not to upset his parents with the terrible news.

Don't think you'd fall for it? Think again. Con artists go to great lengths to fool their victims, including trolling social media sites to learn the names of family members. The swindle is so successful that 1 out of 4 targeted seniors over age 70 pay up.

The solution is for you to hang up and call your relatives directly to verify details.

4 smart strategies to secure your credit

Identity theft comes in many forms. Someone pretending to be you might wipe out your bank account, get a loan, or claim your tax refund. It's no surprise that having your identity stolen can destroy your life. If you want to protect your identity, one of the best things you can do is safeguard your credit. With a little know-how, you can get free reports, make freezes, set fraud alerts, find your credit score, correct wrong information, and more.

Put the freeze on ID thieves. The Federal Trade Commission says credit card fraud is the No. 1 source of identity theft. Fortunately, you have a way to put the kibosh on ID thieves before they open a card in your name.

Contact the three major credit bureaus and tell them to freeze your credit. This shuts off access to your report from anyone but you, preventing fraudsters from opening accounts or borrowing money in your name. There's no charge for the service, but be prepared to answer some questions to verify your identity. You'll need to temporarily lift the freeze if you apply for a loan or credit card.

Place a fraud alert — it's fast and free. If you ever lose your wallet, credit card, or Social Security card, or if your information has been stolen in a data breach, set up a fraud alert on your credit report immediately. This tells credit card companies and lenders to check with you before approving any new line of credit. You only have to notify one of the major credit bureaus, and by law the others are alerted.

Check your credit score with the click of a button. You can get a free copy of your credit report every 12 months from each of the three national credit reporting companies. You have the option of ordering them all at once or requesting one at a time throughout the year. The fastest way to review your report is to head online.

1. Go to *annualcreditreport.com* and click *Request yours now!*

2. Click *Request your credit reports* and fill out the required information.

3. Request a report from any or all of the credit bureaus — Equifax, Experian, and TransUnion.

4. For each report, you'll be asked security questions to verify your identity. You may have to recall loans you've taken out or accounts you've opened.

5. Once you've correctly responded to the questions, the credit agency will generate your report. You can save it to your computer or print it out.

Check for false information to sniff out fraud. Once you have your report, make sure your name and current and former addresses are accurate. Search for accounts that are incorrectly marked as late or have the wrong balances. Be sure all your open accounts are marked as such. If you see a credit card or loan that you don't recognize, you could be a victim of identity theft.

If you find an inaccuracy in your report, contact the lender or business that supplied the incorrect information. Same goes if you believe someone opened an account in your name. If that's the case, close the account, have it flagged for fraud, and initiate a dispute with any of the credit agencies that reported the error. You can contact them online, by phone, and by mail.

Equifax	equifax.com	866-349-5191	P.O. Box 740214 Atlanta GA 30374
Experian	experian.com	888-397-3742	P.O. Box 4500 Allen TX 75013
TransUnion	transunion.com	800-916-8800	P.O. Box 2000 Chester PA 19016

Click at your own risk — top 10 most dangerous links

Many scams are perpetrated over email. For example, scammers may send you a warning that says one of your online accounts is locked. All you have to do is click the link they provide in the body of the email to rectify the problem.

But when you do so, you unwittingly download malware onto your computer or go to a fake website that captures your personal details scammers then use to steal your identity.

One of the best ways to protect your computer, your identity, and your bank account is to learn to spot these fake links. Look closely at the web address they want you to click on. If you can't see the full address, move your cursor over the link and wait for the URL to appear. Do not click on it, simply hover your mouse over it and read the address.

If the link ends in any of the following extensions, you're most likely dealing with a scam.

- *zip*
- *review*
- *country*
- *kim*
- *cricket*
- *science*
- *work*
- *party*
- *gq*
- *link*

Scam websites and fake messages can contain other web addresses. Avoid clicking links in any email unless you are 100% sure you can trust it.

Never put any online account login details or passwords in your will. It creates a security nightmare for your heirs. The reason? After wills go through the probate process, the information in them becomes public knowledge. Anybody could look up your accounts and log in to them. Instead, keep this info separate but secure, like in a home lock box or a bank safe deposit box.

7 ways to thwart medical ID theft

Identity thieves don't just want your credit card information anymore. They're going after your health benefits, too.

According to the Federal Trade Commission (FTC), cases of medical identity theft are becoming much more common. Scammers are stealing information to get medical treatments, prescriptions, or benefits. Fortunately, if you know what they're looking for you can protect yourself against this growing form of fraud.

- Your insurance cards contain sensitive data, so keep them away from prying eyes. Contact your health insurance company immediately if your card is lost or stolen. If you have Medicare, call Social Security at 800-722-1213 to get a replacement card.

- Stay mindful of who you let see or hear your insurance number. As a general rule, anyone who isn't a medical professional should stay in the dark.

- Only enter your insurance info into websites you trust. Look for a little lock icon on the top bar of your web browser. Also make sure the official URL begins with "https."

- Scan all the bills and statements you get from your doctor's office. If you see charges for medicine, treatments, or other services you don't remember, you could be a victim of medical identity theft. Reach out to your insurance company's fraud department immediately.

- Periodically review your medical records and alert your provider if you find errors. To get a copy, submit a written request to your provider and ask about required fees. If they don't send your records to you within 30 days, go to *hhs.gov/ocr* to file a complaint.

- Sign up for fraud alerts from your health insurance company. You'll receive text messages or emails that notify you about activity on your accounts.

- Tear labels off empty pill bottles or black out your info before you toss or recycle them. The prescription label may contain sensitive personal details.

The 4 easiest steps to protect your privacy online

About half of all Baby Boomers worry about keeping their information secure while they're using the internet. Here's how to make sure you stay safe.

1. See to it that your online accounts are set up with secure passwords and two-factor authentication. For more information, see Chapter 16.

2. Install antivirus software on your devices and turn on firewalls to guard your connection.

3. Avoid clicking on any suspicious links in emails, texts, or other messages.

4. Check the privacy settings on your web browser to limit how much of your personal details are stored and shared while you're online. Go to the browser's settings or preferences and look for *Privacy*.

Help from Uncle Sam: Take a bite out of crime

The U.S. government runs several helpful websites that aid in preventing or recovering from identity theft. Check out these three.

- *Consumer.ftc.gov/identity-theft-and-online-security/identity-theft*. This website, run by the Federal Trade Commission (FTC), offers tips on recognizing and preventing identity theft. It also has great info on scams and frauds to watch out for.

- *Usa.gov/identity-theft.* Go here for tips on staying safe from scams and identity thieves, as well as how to report identity theft.

- *Identitytheft.gov.* Find resources and recovery plans for victims of identity theft. If you have had your personal details stolen, go to this website and press the *Get Started* button.

In addition to reporting ID theft online, it's a good idea to contact your local police department. This creates an official record of the issue.

Worried your personal information is being stolen online? Take these steps to virtually disappear from online thieves.

- Delete your social media accounts. If you just stop using social media, the info will still be available online. To truly wipe your profile off of the web, search the settings on each social media platform and completely delete your account. Alternatively, you can take steps to limit who can view your profile. For more info on how to do this, see Chapter 25.

- Search for your name online and see what comes up. If you find any websites that have personal details you don't want shared, reach out to the relevant companies and ask them to take the info off their site.

- Look to see how your online accounts are using your personal data. You may have options to limit what data they access or are allowed to share.

18 Scams

The FBI warns that scams targeting seniors are becoming more and more common. That's because fraudsters and thieves think seniors not only have more money in the bank than younger folk, but may be less tech-savvy and more trusting, as well.

If you want to protect your nest egg from scammers, think twice before you hand over personal information to anyone who doesn't need it and learn how to spot the warning signs that someone is trying to scam you.

3 signs you're being scammed

Scams come in all different shapes and sizes. But most have a few things in common. Be on the lookout for these financial scam red flags, no matter if it's from an email, text message, or phone call.

A major organization is contacting you. Scammers often pose as well-known businesses like your bank, or government agencies like the Social Security Administration or the IRS. However, legitimate companies won't reach out to you and ask for money or sensitive information.

You have to act fast. Many scams start with an urgent request. It could be something as simple as a prize that you need to claim. Or fraudsters may claim you owe them money. If you don't deal with it right away, you're going to miss out or wind up in trouble.

Scammers ramp up the pressure to get what they want, but a legitimate company will give you time to mull things over.

You must pay in a specific — and unusual — way. Many fraudsters will attempt to get you to pay them in gift cards, via money transfer, or using a payment app like PayPal. Others may send a check and ask you to deposit it and wire them the cash.

Do not respond to any communication meeting these red flags and never send any payment. If you must check on an account status, contact the organization directly, using a legitimate phone number or email address.

Don't take the bait: How to foil phishing attacks

Email is a quick, efficient way to contact people, which makes it a popular choice for scammers. They can send out thousands of scam message with the press of a button.

In a scheme known as phishing, fraudsters create fake emails that look like they come from legitimate organizations. They hope you trust the look of the email enough to hand over cash or personal data.

Here's how to avoid getting duped.

Inspect the sender's email address. Phishing emails may look as if they come from companies you know — like Amazon or Google — but they're actually from fake senders.

Can you see the full email address? If not, move your mouse cursor so it hovers over the name of the sender. The email address should match the company it claims to be from.

Watch out for generic greetings. Scammers may say something like "Dear User" or "Client ID" instead of a personal greeting.

Don't fall for the false sense of urgency. Phishing emails want you to act fast before you have a chance to think about whether or not the message is fake. They may warn about deleting your account or missing out on a package delivery. Remember, legitimate organizations will never rush you in this way.

Stay alert for fake links. Carefully hover your mouse over the link they want you to click on, and look at the revealed full web address. If it is not the company's website, delete the message. This takes less than a second and lets you see if an email link to an internet site is safe before you click on it.

Read for errors. Check the contents of the email for grammatical or spelling mistakes. A poorly written email is usually a sign it's not genuine.

If you're still not sure whether or not an email is real, search the web to see if other people have encountered similar scams. Or contact the organization the message is from directly.

Hang up on phone fraud

It may seem a little old-fashioned in the digital age, but phone scams are still a surprisingly common way for fraudsters to cheat people — especially seniors — out of their money.

Let's say someone calls and says, "Hello, we've noticed a problem with your computer." What should you do? Hang up. This common IT support scam attempts to swindle you out of your credit card information or gain remote access to your computer to "fix" it.

Watch out for these other scenarios.

- Bank scams. You get a call saying there's an issue with your account and you'll need to give your login details to fix it.

- Tax scams. The caller needs your personal details in order to process your tax refund.

- "Anti-Scam" scams. The caller says he's offering compensation and assistance to people who have been a victim of online scams. However, this is actually just another swindle.

Yes, you can rein in robocalls

You're on the National Do Not Call list, so why are you still getting so many robocalls? You know, those annoying communications autodialed by a computer program delivering some prerecorded message. You may be surprised to learn The Federal Trade Commission (FTC) registry only applies to sales calls — not charities, debt collectors, surveys, or political organizations. And certainly not from scammers.

But you can still put the kibosh on calls from anyone or any organization with little more than the push of a button.

- Turn on your phone's option to block unknown or private numbers. Many cellphones come with settings that prevent calls from ringing through if the number is not in your contacts list. Some phones will only send these directly to voicemail.

- Restrict a specific number that has already called by going into your phone log, history, or list of recent callers. Select the offending number and follow the prompts to block it. Some carriers might have a limit on how many numbers you can block.

- Download a robocall blocker app from your smartphone's linked app store.

When a strange number shows up on your caller ID, you may be tempted to answer. The safe bet is to not answer the call, but note the number. Use this for a web search to see if there is any information related to the number. If it is a scam, there will almost certainly be details about it on the internet. If possible, block the number on your phone, or contact the Do Not Call list to inform them about it at *donotcall.gov.*

Shysters are always developing new schemes and ploys to swindle people out of their hard-earned dollars. They often turn to the news for hot topics and pressing issues that will grab your attention — and open your wallet.

For example, some new scams involve cryptocurrencies like Bitcoin and Ethereum. Others use natural disasters to pose as emergency relief companies and organizations.

Beware these 3 Social Security swindles

Scammers want your Social Security number (SSN) so they can open credit cards in your name, access your bank accounts, and more. These three common schemes will try to get you to hand over this confidential information.

- Phishing emails may claim there is an issue with your Social Security number. A link takes you to a fake website that asks for your personal info. Bingo — they have your data. Never click any link in an email like this or type your SSN into a strange website. Call the Social Security Administration (SSA) or go straight to their website to check things out.

- You receive a message prompting you to create a new Social Security Account. Remember, the government will never email asking you to do this. Instead, go to *ssa.gov/myaccount/create* to set one up.

- Scammers pretending to work for the SSA say your benefits will stop unless you get their new, high-tech Social Security card. However, no such thing exists.

Lonely hearts look out: Don't fall for romance scam

Millions of people use online dating services to find a mate. But scoundrels scour these websites for an opportunity to steal your heart and your savings.

This is how it works. Scammers create fake profiles to get in touch with you, and when the time is right, profess their love. Then they claim to need cash for, say, a medical emergency or airfare to visit you. They take your money — usually via a wire transfer or gift cards — but there's no surgery or trip.

This common scheme has cost Americans over $143 million. Spot the warning signs so you don't become a victim.

- Somebody you have met online or on a dating app declares strong feelings for you after a short period of time.

- The person's circumstances mirror your own. For example, they may have some of the same medical issues.

- They suggest moving conversations to a private channel so there is less scrutiny.

- They are reluctant to meet face-to-face or to video chat.

- Eventually they claim there's an emergency or situation that requires a large sum of money. They may initially refuse your offer to help, then change their mind.

Avoid falling for this scam by proceeding slowly with any new relationship. Meet in person or by video chat, and never hand over large sums of money. If you suspect someone you're talking to may be trying to pull a romance scam, sever contact immediately.

Rip-off rebound: What to do after the con

If you are the victim of a scam, help is at hand. Take these important steps as soon as possible.

Report the scam. Reach out to any or all of these organizations.

- the Federal Trade Commission (FTC) at *reportfraud.ftc.gov*

- your State Consumer Protection Office at *usa.gov/ state-consumer*

- your local police department

Stop the money. If you paid the scammer, you may be able to halt the transfer of funds or reverse the transaction. Contact your bank, credit card company, or the company you used to make the payment.

19 Wi-Fi

Wireless internet — also called Wi-Fi — allows you to connect computers, tablets, smartphones, and other devices to the internet without cables. It's commonplace in most homes. In fact, one survey found that the average household has 22 devices wirelessly connected to the internet.

While convenient, it may not always be secure. If you don't set up your network properly, anyone within range of your Wi-Fi signal could access the devices you have linked to your home internet. Fortunately, with the right knowledge, you can ensure your connection is protected against hackers.

Change these settings to defend your network

A Wi-Fi router allows you to connect to the internet wirelessly. Most of these devices work right out of the box, but to be truly secure from hackers you'll need to change some of the default settings. Here's how to access the router control panel to view all the settings, change the network name, set up a new password, and more.

1. Find your router's Internet Protocol (IP) address. This is usually located somewhere on the body of your router. It will be a string of numbers separated by periods, such as 192.68.0.1. If the IP address is not immediately obvious, perform a web search using the name of your router's manufacturer.

2. Using a web browser on your computer, tablet, or smartphone, enter the IP address into the URL bar and hit Enter.

This will bring up your router's control panel. The look will vary depending on the brand of your router.

3. Click on the *Settings* tab.

4. Enter the router's default admin password located on the back of your router. This allows you to change settings.

5. Click on the *Wireless* option under the *Settings* or *Advanced Settings* tab.

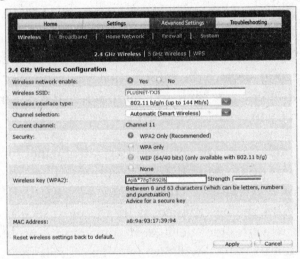

Now you're ready to amp up the security on your router.

Change the name. The default name of your network is set up by the router's manufacturer, and if you leave it in place, hackers could get a valuable clue that would help them access your internet.

To enter a new name, look for the box labeled *Network Name* or *Wireless SSID*. This should display the current network name. Click on this box and type in a new name. You can choose something fun and easy to recognize, but anyone who can access the signal will see your network's name. So avoid using any personal details, such as your street address or date of birth.

Pick a new Wi-Fi password. This allows devices to connect to the internet though your router. Since the default password is sometimes clearly printed on the router, anyone with physical access to your home or office could use it to access your internet — unless you change it.

Look for the box labeled *Wireless Key, Password,* or *Shared Key* in the router control panel. Click on it and type in a new password. For tips on creating strong passwords and keeping track of them, see Chapter 16.

Set up encryption. Your Wi-Fi router is the link between all your computing devices and the internet. One of the best security strategies is to make sure the information you send and receive is encrypted. Routers have built-in encryption features, but you may need to turn them on.

Check the *Settings* page in your router control panel for a box or field that shows your router's security options. There are three main types of encryption to choose from — WEP, WPA, and WPA2. WPA2 is the best choice, as it's the most secure, but it may cause problems with older devices. If you run into problems while using it, switch to WPA. Avoid using WEP, as it is the least secure.

After you have finished securing your Wi-Fi network, click on the *Apply* button to save your changes.

The router admin password you use to log into your router's control panel is different from the Wi-Fi password you'll use to log your devices into your internet. In addition to the Wi-Fi password, change the admin password as soon as possible. Take care of this in the *Settings* section, as well.

Fire up your firewall for ultimate security

Firewalls act as barriers between your devices and the internet. They block unwanted viruses and other malicious software from getting through. While you can install a software firewall on your computer, your router also has one. It is usually turned on by default, but it doesn't hurt to check and make sure it's working. Here's how.

1. Enter your router's IP address into a web browser's URL bar to open the router control panel.

2. Click on the *Settings* or *Advanced Settings* tab and log in.

3. Click on *Firewall*. Check to make sure that it is turned on. If not, click the *Enable* button and select *Apply*.

Keep your router out of reach

Strong passwords and firewalls aren't all you need to keep your Wi-Fi router safe. If this device is too close to an accessible public area, like a sidewalk, it may be easy for hackers to get within range of your Wi-Fi signal.

Install your router in a room far enough from public areas that the signal cannot be accessed by anyone else, but positioned so it can still reach all of your own devices.

20 Online shopping safety

Americans spend close to $1 trillion shopping online every year. If you were to lay that many dollar bills from end to end, they could stretch from the Earth to the sun.

It's easy to see why online shopping is so popular. While relaxing in your favorite armchair, you can quickly and conveniently select from hundreds of thousands of products.

But beware — all that money is bound to attract scammers, hackers, and other thieves.

Security check: 2 signs a site is fortified

Online shopping has many advantages. You can easily compare prices, find good deals, choose from a wide range of options, plus get products delivered right to your doorstep. But there are some security issues you need to consider, too.

Paying for an online transaction with your credit card means everything needs to be as secure as possible. You don't want your money or financial information stolen while you're shopping. Always check for these two things before using your credit card online.

- Make sure the website address starts with "https" instead of just "http." The "s" stands for secure, and indicates there are protections in place guaranteeing safe credit card transactions.

- Look for a padlock icon in the address bar at the top of the web page. This indicates the connection is encrypted, so all information that travels between you and the website is protected. Click on this padlock icon for more security details and information about the website's security settings.

You're away from home and pop into a local coffee shop or library to use their free Wi-Fi. No big deal. Many businesses have a guest internet connection available, and will give out the password to their customers. What could be wrong with that?

Nothing, as long as you only use these public connections for harmless web surfing.

Hackers find it incredibly easy to gain access to these public Wi-Fi signals, and then monitor whatever you do while you're connected. That means they may be able to get your financial information, passwords, and other details if you log into an account or do any online shopping.

Paying with plastic? Don't miss this inside info

Even if you know a website is secure, never use a debit card to pay online. They offer less protection than credit cards if the information is stolen. You could even be responsible for all the fraudulent charges — depending on how quickly you report the theft.

But that's not the case with a credit card. If you notify your bank of the fraud quickly enough, you're not on the hook for anything that thieves spend.

Still, take extra steps to ensure your financial info is safe while shopping.

Use a virtual credit card number. Instead of giving out your actual credit card number, you input a randomly generated number tied to your card. That way thieves won't have access to your money if your financial info is exposed in a data breach. Check with your credit card issuer to see if they offer this service.

Put your cards in a digital wallet. Heard of PayPal? What about Google Pay, Apple Pay, or Samsung Pay? These are examples of digital wallets, sometimes called e-wallets, which let you link a credit card to an app on your smartphone or computer. You then use the app to make a purchase without ever giving the vendor your account details.

Set up transaction alerts. Your credit card issuer can send you a text, email, or other notification whenever your card is used to make a purchase. This is a great way to catch fraudulent transactions and report them right away.

Spot these red flags to avoid phony reviews

Amazon is one of the best known and most successful online retailers in the world. In addition to thousands of products, on its website you'll also find customer reviews designed to help you select the perfect item. But you may be surprised to learn that, according to one estimate, up to 42% of the reviews on this site are fake. A recent study claims that bogus reviews can cause people to seriously overpay for bad products.

Even though Amazon banned sellers from paying for five-star reviews, many companies still skirt these rules. Fortunately, it's easy to spot the signs of a fake review — once you know what to watch for.

- Vague words and phrases — such as "I love it!" or "Great!" — rather than specific details about the product.

- Reviews that use extreme adjectives. Real people don't tend to gush about the items they buy.

- Mentions of competing products and businesses.

- Reviews that all sound similar or use the same words.

To get a better idea of whether or not a product is worth buying, scan some of the less positive reviews. But bear in mind that some people post negative reviews for malicious reasons. If there's a small percentage of negative reviews, disregard them.

Research the product on other online sites as well, to find independent, expert reviews and a more in-depth look at the flaws and features.

Received an email containing a special offer that sounds too good to be true? It probably is.

In this common scam, the email looks like a deal from a trusted online retailer. The message claims all you have to do is click on the link to claim this bargain. Once you do, you're connected to a fake website and the fraudsters have their hooks into you.

Always check the sender's information by hovering your mouse cursor over the email address. If it's not actually from the retailer, delete the email immediately. If you're still in doubt, go directly to the retailer's official website to see if the offer is listed there.

Fake site or real deal: 6 ways to tell

Fraudsters can create convincing and sophisticated fake shopping websites. They offer seemingly great deals and offers to lure you in. However, any products you order are never delivered. And, to make matters worse, now thieves have your credit card details. If you want to avoid falling for this common scam, learn how to spot these sham websites.

- Look closely at the website address. Phony sites often use a variation of a well-known product name to make them seem more authentic. For example, a scammer claiming to sell Apple products could use the address *iphonebargains.com*.

- Watch out for offers that seem too good to be true. Compare prices to see if they are similar across the web. If one site has suspiciously low prices, it could be a red flag.

- Check for a Contact Us page at the bottom of the website. Do the details look genuine? If you can find a physical business address, do a web search to verify it actually exists.

- Avoid websites that ask you to pay by bank transfer. This payment method gives you no consumer protection. If you use a credit card, you can dispute fraudulent charges with your bank.

- Make sure there is a return policy. Many bogus websites won't bother including one on their page.

- Do a web search to find reviews of the site. Some, like *trustpilot.com*, contain reviews of online sites and businesses. See if other people reported being scammed or having their information stolen by the online store you're researching.

Whenever you buy something online, you have to enter an email address — so you can get your receipt, as well as status updates about your order. The downside is many online retailers will then bombard you with special offers and other marketing emails.

An easy way to avoid this is to simply create an email address you only use for online shopping. You can do this for free with a web-based service, like Gmail.

Use this address whenever you don't want to give retailers your personal email.

21 Viruses, spyware, and malware

The tech world faces a constant, seemingly endless battle for the safety of all computer users. Companies are always creating new devices and software to help protect your personal data while hackers and cybercriminals work to discover new security flaws. These thieves use malicious software — otherwise known as malware — to disrupt computer networks, damage devices, and steal valuable financial or personal information. Take steps now to secure your personal data and protect your computer from viruses.

Outsmart malware with this security checklist

Cybercriminals are constantly creating new pieces of malware designed to infect your computer. The exact way these nasty bugs can infiltrate your devices and steal your info depends on what you're dealing with. Here are some of the most common types of malware.

- Worms are designed to replicate themselves and spread between computers. They may perform nuisance tasks, like taking up space on your computer to make it virtually unusable. Some may install other programs that can steal sensitive data.

- Trojans hide in harmless programs, such as games, apps, or fake advertisements which pop up on your computer. But once you click on, download, or enter personal information, they infect your computer with malicious software designed to steal your data or damage your devices.

- Spyware is a very sophisticated type of virus that, once it has infected your computer, analyzes all of the data there and sends it back to its author. This includes not just files of information but also keystrokes entered on websites. This is known as key-logging and it enables the spyware to identify login details and passwords. Worse still, due to the sophistication of spyware, you probably will not even be aware that this is happening.

- Ransomware blocks access to your files or causes your computer to stop working entirely. Pop-up messages will offer to fix the problem — for a price. If you are the victim of a ransomware attack, don't hand over any money online. Take your computer to an expert for help.

These important security measures can help you make sure malware doesn't find a way into your computer, phone, or tablet.

Be wary of unsolicited messages. Hackers will often use emails or text messages to lure you into accidentally downloading viruses. Don't open any links or attachments in messages from senders you don't recognize.

Guard your login details. Don't enter your passwords or email address into strange pop-up windows or websites you don't recognize. Also avoid logging in to accounts while you're connected to public Wi-Fi.

Don't download apps from just anywhere. Only download software from your device's linked app store or other trusted sources. It's easy to accidentally pick up a virus when you get files from sketchy websites.

7 warning signs your computer is infected

Recognize the symptoms of viruses and malware so you can act fast and take care of the problem before it gets out of control. Watch out for these common red flags.

- Your computer has problems starting up. It may turn on and then immediately shut down again.

- You experience freezes or crashes frequently, and can't pin-point a reason why.

- Generally, you experience poor performance during everyday tasks. Your device may feel sluggish when you try to open apps, work on documents, or save files.

- Random error messages keep appearing on your screen.

- You notice a lot of pop-up ads on the screen.

- Files and folders you don't remember deleting are missing from your computer.

- Random emails are sent to the contacts in your address book. You may only find out about this if you are contacted by someone who receives one of these strange messages.

Wipe out viruses with these simple steps

If your computer is infected with malware, don't panic. You can take a few simple steps to remove the virus. Here's how.

For PC users. Microsoft has built-in antivirus software that can help you detect and clean up viruses. If you suspect your computer has malware on it, use this program to sweep your files and track it down.

1. Open your Windows Security settings.

2. Select Virus & threat protection > Scan options.

3. Click on *Windows Defender Offline scan* and select *Scan now*. The scan will take about 15 minutes. After it is over, your computer will restart.

The scan should automatically remove or quarantine any malware that it finds. To see the results of the scan, open Windows Security settings and go to Virus & threat protection > Protection history.

For Mac users. Windows computers are more likely to be targeted by viruses and other malware, but Macs aren't immune to these threats. If you do suspect your Mac has a virus, make sure your operating system is up to date.

Apple has built in antivirus protection called Xprotect. It usually updates automatically, but older versions of macOS may no longer be supported by Apple. To see if you can update your Mac, go to the Apple menu, select *System Preferences* and click on *Software Update*.

Xprotect will automatically scan your files and will warn you if it detects potential malware. It will also block the software and give you the option to move the infected file to the Trash.

However, when new viruses are developed, they may be able to bypass this security for days — or even weeks — before Apple is able to develop a fix. If you suspect your computer is infected, use a trusted third-party antivirus software to scan your computer for malware.

Don't let fake apps infect your phone

With the evolution of technology, smartphones and tablets are really just mini computers. And that makes them a prime target for hackers. Malware may infect mobile devices through text messages, emails, or even webpages, but one of the biggest dangers to watch out for is spyware embedded in fake apps.

These bogus programs may pose as harmless software — perhaps photo editing tools or even a flashlight app. When you download it, you may be prompted to link it with your social media accounts, for instance. If you do, hackers can access your login data and steal your passwords.

While the official app stores for Apple devices and Androids do their best to remove these malicious programs, some still slip through the cracks. Here's how to spot them.

- Make sure it's the real deal. Scammers create apps that have names and icons that are similar to popular, trusted apps. If you notice mistakes in the app description, or if the title is slightly off, avoid downloading it.

- Look beneath the name of the app to find its developer. Do a quick web search to see if this is a reputable company. Many app stores also let you tap on the developer's name to see what other products they have made.

- Watch out for apps that request a lot of access to your phone. Fake ones may ask you to grant them permission to tap into accounts and data they shouldn't need. For example, ask yourself why a flashlight would need access to social media or your location data.

Viruses most commonly find their way onto your computer through the internet. One of the best ways to ensure your connection is protected is to use a firewall. It works by monitoring your internet connection and blocking any suspicious traffic.

Most computers have a built-in firewall. Activate it by going to the Settings app on Windows or System Settings on a Mac and searching for "firewall."

Antivirus programs can also have built-in firewalls that add another layer of security to your computer.

Create a cyberdefense — for free

The internet is riddled with spyware and other viruses that can infect your computer. If you want to protect your identity and information, a smart move is to vaccinate your PC with antivirus software. The best part? If you know where to look, finding great protection is fast and easy. These companies offer free protection against viruses and malware.

- Avast at *avast.com*

- Panda at *pandasecurity.com*

- Spybot Search & Destroy at *safer-networking.org/products/spybot-free-edition*

- SpywareBlaster at *brightfort.com/spywareblaster*

- SUPERAntiSpyware at *superantispyware.com/free-edition.html*

Major companies also offer paid antivirus software that comes with extra features. If you're not sure what option is best for you, consider these tips.

Opt for something that doesn't tax your computer. If you notice your device feels sluggish after you download a new antivirus app, it may be taking up too much of your system's resources. Try using a different app.

Consider the features you need. Some antivirus software may offer protection for additional devices, parental controls that limit screen time, and password managers to help you keep track of login details. If you don't need these extra bells and whistles, choose something simpler.

Think about customer service support. Paid antivirus software often has help lines and customer service reps you can call at any time. Free versions may skimp on this.

Look at the company's privacy statements. Antivirus software has to access a lot of sensitive information on your computer. You want to make sure the company you choose is smart about keeping that data safe and secure. Go to the company's website and read the privacy policies to see what they do with your information.

Hackers are constantly creating new, more sophisticated viruses. Make sure you're protected from the newest threats by keeping your antivirus software up to date. Most programs allow you to turn on automatic updates whenever your device is connected to the internet.

Chapter 22 Web browser security

A web browser is your portal to the internet. Browsers — such as Google Chrome, Microsoft Edge, Mozilla Firefox, and Safari — allow you to surf the web, shop online, and more. But every time you connect to the internet, you open yourself up to all sorts of online threats.

Your computer constantly sends and receives data while hooked up to the web, allowing hackers and other scammers the opportunity to infect your device with viruses or other malware.

You don't need to get off the web to stay safe, though. Activating firewalls, installing antivirus software, and staying alert to fake websites help you dodge some of the most dangerous threats. And if you know how to set up your web browser properly, it can be a powerful way to protect your privacy and thwart hackers.

Beef up browser settings for added protection

Web browser programs have powerful privacy settings designed to keep you safe and secure while you're online. Here's how to find them.

1. Open your browser — this could be something like Microsoft Edge, Mozilla Firefox, Google Chrome, or Safari — and click on the menu buttons usually found across the top of your screen. Look for a *Settings* or *Preferences* option. Click on it.

2. Click on the *Privacy and security* menu to see the full range of options. This may have a different name depending on which browser you are using. Now start exploring.

Most browsers have general privacy sets you can choose from. The strictest will crack down on security, but can cause certain websites to load slowly or not work at all.

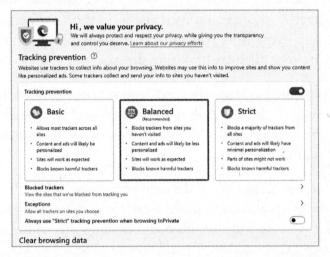

You also have the option to change individual settings, to ensure your privacy is protected while you browse. Check out these important ones.

Pop-up windows. Many browsers can automatically block annoying ads from appearing. If you enable the pop-up blocker, it may also bar certain notifications or login screens.

Cookies. These are small files that websites use to track, personalize, and save information about what you look at and click on. Retailers may use cookies to record which items you put in your virtual shopping cart or to keep a log of your past purchases.

The bad news is some hackers use them to spy on your browsing history. You may want to disable third-party cookies so your information can't be tracked across different sites. However, if you turn off all cookies, you could encounter problems with many webpages.

Suspicious websites. If you have a feature that blocks fake websites or potential attacks, turn it on. This can keep you from accidentally connecting to pages that aren't secure or may have dangerous malware hidden on them.

Camera and microphone permissions. Certain websites may try to automatically access your device's camera or microphone. This makes sense for video chatting, but it can also be used by hackers to spy on people. Set it so your browser asks before it lets any website turn on your camera or record sound.

HTTPS only mode. This setting ensures that any time you use a website your connection is encrypted. That makes it much harder for thieves to steal the information going between your computer and the site. If a website doesn't offer the highest security, your browser will warn you before opening the page.

Want to virtually vanish from the internet? Then turn on private or incognito mode in your browser. This keeps websites from tracking your internet activity and doesn't save passwords, login info, or even your search history.

It's important to realize, however, this won't make your internet usage completely private. Your internet provider can still see the traffic on your network. And your connection still may be compromised by hackers, viruses, or malware. But private mode is a great way to browse the web if you're using a public computer or if you want to research a sensitive topic.

To turn on this mode in most browsers, go to the *File* menu in the top toolbar. Press *New Private Window* or *New Incognito Window*.

If you're always using private mode, you may want to consider switching to a third-party browser that doesn't track your searches. DuckDuckGo and Startpage are two common choices.

A zippier web experience — without risk

Modern browsers allow you to install add-ons, plug-ins, and extensions to give you a few extra features. Some block ads, some track down coupons, while others change the appearance of the websites you visit. Many are helpful tools — but some could pose a danger to your online security.

They work by installing a little bit of extra code to your browser. And that means hackers could use them to sneak malware onto your computer. Others may have security flaws that let thieves bypass your browser's security measures. So how can you make sure you're using them safely?

Stay official. Only install software from authorized web stores. While it's not a perfect guarantee the extension is safe, security experts do their best to research and vet add-ons before they are added to the store.

Show restraint. Don't put too many extensions on your browser. The more you download, the more opportunities hackers have to find a way in to your computer.

Get the rundown. Research the extension and the company who made it. If you find reviews that warn about data being stolen or computer problems, avoid that extension.

Limit access. Consider what permissions the extension needs. Any that request unnecessary information, or suddenly want to extend their access after being installed, could harbor malware.

Here's how to add extensions and other add-ons to your browser.

1. Open your browser and click on the Menu button. Look for an option that says *Extensions* or *Add-ons*. It may look some-thing like this depending on which browser you use.

   ⟨3 Extensions

2. Look for a button to open the browser's web store. Click it to view available add-ons.

3. Click on any extension to view more details about it. If you want to add it to your browser, click the *Add* or *Get* button.

To manage any extensions you have, go to the browser menu and find *Manage extensions*, *Add-ons*, or look for this icon in the top toolbar.

Click it to view the add-ons you have installed. You can deactivate and delete any that you no longer use.

23 Backups and cloud services

Your computer, tablet, and smartphone hold hundreds of important documents, photos, and other files. Chances are, you don't have hard copies of all of them. If something serious happens to one of your devices, can you risk losing these items?

That's why you need to perform backups on a regular basis — at least once a week. You'll have a copy of everything you saved even if your device is lost, stolen, or damaged.

Crash insurance: 2 smart backup solutions

One of the easiest ways to create a copy of all your files is to back up your device to an external, or removable, drive. Here are the two main types of removable storage.

Flash drives. Sometimes known as thumb drives, these are small, portable devices that can easily fit into a pocket. Despite their size, modern flash drives offer plenty of storage. You can find some that hold over a terabyte (TB) of data, which is more than enough for most home users.

External hard drives. These tend to be larger and offer even more storage — easily enough room to back up the entire contents of a computer. Transferring files is quicker with an external hard drive, but they are more expensive and less portable than flash drives.

To back up your files, connect either an external drive or flash drive to your computer using the USB port. Copy and paste or drag the files you want to back up into the removable drive icon that appears on your desktop.

Storing an external drive safely is paramount. You don't want the data on it lost, stolen, or damaged. Consider these options.

- Perhaps you already own a home safe to keep small valuable items and other important documents secure. If not, this is a smart investment. Look for one that is protected against fire and water damage. Some home safes also come with bolt down kits so they are harder to steal.

- Give your external drive to a trusted friend or family member. This way your files are stored far away from your computer, so if something happens to your home you don't have to worry about losing your backup, too.

- A bank safe deposit box is a trickier choice. While completely removed from your home and totally secure, this method makes it difficult to frequently create new backups. Unless you make frequent trips to the bank with replacement backups, you may lose newer files if anything happens to your computer.

5 reasons to keep your data safe in the cloud

Cloud storage services hold backup content remotely in secure servers. They have grown increasingly popular in recent years, and it's easy to see why. Here are some of the main benefits to backing up your data using the cloud.

- Files can be automatically backed up. Whenever your computer, phone, or tablet is turned on and connected to Wi-Fi, copies of your files will be automatically saved and stored to a remote server.

- You're able to access files saved to a cloud service from anywhere and from any device — as long as it's connected to the internet.

- You can share content on your cloud server with friends and family members.

- Many of the main tech companies have cloud services that offer some free storage if you own one of their devices.

- You never have to worry about transferring files to external drives or bothering with secure storage for them.

Windows users — don't miss this free service

Microsoft offers 5 gigabytes (GB) of free storage with their OneDrive service if you have a Windows device. All you need to access it is a Microsoft Account. There are a few different ways to use it, but any content saved in your OneDrive is available in all of these locations, as long as you are signed in to your Microsoft Account.

- Click on OneDrive in the File Explorer or in the Start Menu. Save files directly to OneDrive from your computer or copy and paste them into this folder.

- Download the OneDrive app from the Microsoft Store. Open the app and select this button to add files or folders to it.

- Go online to *onedrive.live.com* and log in with your Microsoft Account. Select the *Upload* button at the top of the screen to add files.

To make changes to OneDrive, click on the cloud icon in your Taskbar.

Click on the gear icon to access the Settings menu, view more features, and manage your account.

OneDrive has a Personal Vault section that's great for storing sensitive documents and files. Anything here is encrypted for increased protection. To unlock the Personal Vault, you will need a fingerprint scan, email code, or other form of two-factor identification.

iCloud gives you peace of mind

Apple's cloud storage service, known as iCloud, is a great option for anyone with a Mac, iPhone, or iPad. You'll need an Apple ID to use this service, but once you set it up, you get 5GB of free storage.

Follow these steps to start saving your files.

1. Open the Settings app — called System settings if you are on a computer running macOS Ventura — and select *Apple ID, iCloud, Media & Purchases*.

2. Click or tap on *iCloud*.

3. Select the items you want to save. You can choose to save your photo library, emails, and more. Select the *Show All* option to view more categories.

4. To create an automatic backup for the entire contents of your devices, select the iCloud backup option. Turn the option for *Back Up This [device name]* to the on position.

Open files you save to your iCloud account directly from any of your linked Apple devices or from any other computer by going online to *icloud.com* and using your Apple ID to log in.

Google simplifies cloud storage

Every Google Account comes equipped with 15GB of free storage. This is a great option when you want to back up files from your computer, tablet, or smartphone.

But if that's not enough space — and you don't mind paying for it — get more storage and extra perks by subscribing to a Google One plan.

It's super easy to set up automated backups since Google cloud storage works seamlessly with Google Photos, Gmail, and Google Drive, a service for creating and storing spreadsheets, slideshows, and word documents.

To back up a phone or tablet using Google One, download the app from the Google Play Store or the Apple's App Store.

Need more storage? Upgrade to iCloud+ for a monthly subscription fee. In addition, you'll also get these enhanced security features.

- Private Relay. This protects your information when you browse the web with Safari.

- Hide My Email. When you sign up for a website that requires an email, you can choose to create a random one. Messages will be forwarded to your primary email account so advertisers and other online services can't see your personal info.

Cloud control: Dropbox is fast and secure

Dropbox is an independent cloud service that isn't tied to a specific operating system. Free accounts offer 2GB of storage while paid plans provide a range of options and perks.

Download the Dropbox app from any licensed app store, or go online to *dropbox.com* to start saving files in the cloud. You'll need to create an account with a username and a secure password.

Once content has been added to your Dropbox account, access it from any device by logging into the Dropbox app or going to the website.

Top 10 Tips for Digital Security

1. Never give out online bank account details and never use your debit card online via public Wi-Fi.

2. Create passwords that are unique and include a mix of letters, numbers, and special characters. Use a password manager for added security.

3. Treat your personal details with great caution, as they could be a gold mine for anyone trying to steal your identity and commit fraud.

4. Never respond to an unsolicited email, text message, or phone call with any personal or financial information.

5. Your Wi-Fi router is a potential gateway for hackers into your computing devices. Keep it secure by changing its network name and password.

6. Stay safe when shopping online by looking for "https" in the website address and a padlock icon in the web address box.

7. Your computer could be infected with a virus if apps disappear, its speed becomes suspiciously slow, error messages and pop-up ads keep appearing, or it continually closes down for no reason.

8. Install antivirus software and keep it up to date so you can stay on top of the latest computer viruses.

9. Enable a firewall on your computer to prevent malicious software infecting it through your web browser.

10. Back up all your most important files, documents, and photos. Use a cloud service, a flash drive, or an external hard drive.

Staying Connected

24 Email

Over 300 billion emails are sent worldwide every day. This popular form of electronic communication is used for everything from business correspondence to staying in touch with friends.

If you need an email account, webmail services are a popular choice. You can access them from any device that's connected to the internet and synchronize your email across all your devices. Best of all — these accounts are free. Check out some popular options.

- Gmail at *mail.google.com*

- Yahoo! Mail at *mail.yahoo.com*

- iCloud at *icloud.com/mail*

- Outlook at *outlook.live.com/mail*

- AOL at *mail.aol.com*

Webmail services also have companion apps you can use independently of the online webpage. Any emails sent from the app will be available on your email's website, and vice versa.

Search for your email service in your device's app store. Then download the app to your phone or tablet and access your mail from anywhere.

4 steps to 'you've got mail'

After you select an email service, you'll create an account. Follow these simple steps to set one up.

1. Go online to the webmail's home page. For example, if you want to create a Gmail account, you'll go to *mail.google.com*.

2. Create a username. Choose something easy to remember that your friends and family can recognize. You can use your full name, but you may need to include a number or two if you have a common name, JohnSmith75 for example. Don't put personal information — such as your birthday — in your username.

3. Choose a secure password. Make sure it's at least 12 characters long and has a mix of symbols, numbers, and upper and lowercase letters.

4. Some email services will require your birthday, phone number, or another email to finish setting up the account. This info may be used to verify your identity and reset your password if you ever lose access to the account.

You'll use the same credentials to log in to your account whether on the webpage or the companion app you've downloaded to your mobile device.

Pull the plug on hackers

Email accounts are a treasure trove of personal information. If a hacker manages to get into yours, it's a few short steps for them to lock you out. Then they can follow links to find bank account, credit card, and health information. Fortunately, you can easily keep your email safe and secure.

- Make your account passwords as tough as possible — at least 12 characters long, with a mixture of letters, numbers, and symbols.

- If you are asked to create a security question when setting up your email account, make it difficult to guess. If you don't think you can remember the answer, write it down somewhere and keep it in a safe place.

- Avoid including sensitive financial information or personal details — such as your Social Security number or bank account information — in the body of any message you send.

- Use antivirus software that has tools and options for identifying phishing emails and other dangerous scams.

Scam artists often use fake messages and emails to get unsuspecting victims to hand over their personal details and hard-earned cash. But if you want to know the best way to stay safe when using email, follow this simple rule.

Delete any email from unknown senders. Don't open it, and under no circumstances should you click on any links in the email or respond to the sender.

Most email services have an option to mark messages as junk or spam. Do this and any future emails from that sender will go straight to your junk mail folder.

Write it right: Essential skills for messaging

The basics of emailing haven't changed much since the process was first introduced way back in 1971. But if you're rusty, here's a primer.

1. Open your email app or go online to your webmail address.

2. Click or tap on the *New email* button. It may be a + icon in certain apps or email clients.

3. Click or tap in the box labeled *To* and enter the email address for the recipient. If this info is stored in your Contacts app, their details may appear as you type. Simply click or tap on the recipient to enter it into the box.

4. Type relevant topic details in the *Subject* line. This is the only thing that will alert the recipient to the email's contents, so a short, clear phrase can help ensure your email gets read.

5. Enter your message in the main text window of the email. Reread carefully for any typos or mistakes.

6. Once you're ready, click or tap on the *Send* button. Some email clients use an envelope icon.

Want to respond directly to an email you've received? Click on the *Reply* button in the toolbar at the top of the message.

The sender of the original email will automatically appear in the *To* box, and the contents of the original email will go below your new message.

When replying to an email with multiple recipients, you have the option to select *Reply All*.

Be careful when choosing this since your response will be sent to every single person on the original message's recipient list.

Signed, sealed, delivered — attach a file with ease

Emails aren't only for written messages. They're a great way to send images, videos, and other documents. To add these attachments to an email, go to the toolbar located at the top or bottom of your email window. Depending on which email service you use, it will look something like this.

Press the paperclip icon on the toolbar to attach files from your  computer to the message. It's a good idea to add the attachments to your email before you enter a recipient. That way you won't accidentally send an email before you attach the required file.

3 simple tricks stop spammers

Nearly 15 billion spam emails are sent out every day. So if you want to keep your inbox from filling up with junk mail, learn to fight back against spammers. Check out these easy ways to slash the number of unwelcome emails you receive.

Unsubscribe from mailing lists. Online shoppers know you have to enter your email address to complete a purchase. That's just how business is done over the internet. But it also means you're likely to receive a lot of emails from those same retailers.

While this can be a great way to learn about sales, these messages can overwhelm your inbox. To stop these offers from coming in, look at the bottom of the email and see if there is an *Unsubscribe* button. If so, click on it and follow the instructions.

Set up your spam filter. Open your email client's settings and look for a place to block addresses from known spammers, set up filters and blockers that can flag and remove messages that seem suspicious, and more. Take some time to look through these settings so you can make your email more secure.

If you are using Gmail, the spam filter tab will look like this. It may appear different if you are using another email service.

Train your email client to recognize spam. Whenever you receive a spam message, you can usually right-click or press on an email to open up a menu. Flag the message as spam. Over time, your email service will learn to filter out similar emails.

If you use a public computer to check your email, like at an internet café or a library, always log out of your account when you're done. Otherwise anyone who uses the computer after you could access your email account.

25 Social media

Social media is a term for the various websites and apps that allow you to share information and ideas in virtual communities. People use social media to stay in touch with others. Businesses use it to market and promote their products and track customer issues.

Millions of people across the globe link through social media. In fact, experts estimate that 6 out of every 10 people worldwide use some form of it.

A big reason seniors flock to social media platforms such as Facebook and Instagram is these are quick, easy, and free ways to connect with friends and family, especially when you can't see them in person.

Access social media websites by going directly to them online. Create an account, log in, and view content. Companion apps are also a great way to access your social media accounts on your mobile device. When you log in to the app, you'll see the same content as when you log in to the website. To find these apps, go to your device's linked app store and search for the name of your favorite social media platform.

Social graces: How to behave wisely online

Navigating the unwritten rules of social media can be tricky, even for the most experienced and tech-savvy users. These tips can help you practice good online etiquette.

Edit before you post. Think twice before you share anything that might be offensive. No matter how strict your privacy settings are, treat all you say on social media as if every friend and family member will see it.

Stay out of "flame wars." This is a slang term for online arguments conducted over social media. It's easy for them to quickly get out of hand, and unfortunately, anybody can see your argument.

Even if you delete your comments or posts, someone could have taken a screenshot first. And that can live forever in the digital world.

Don't share without permission. Details or pictures of someone else should be considered private. Posting these not only violates their rights, but could give hackers and scammers confidential information.

4 secrets to safe posting

The point of social media is to share news with your friends and family. But if you share too much, you may wind up accidentally leaking personal details or financial information to scammers and hackers. So if you don't want to get yourself in trouble, learn how to strike the right balance.

Check your photos carefully before you post them. It's easy to miss a credit card statement or utility bill in the background of a photo, but eagle-eyed scammers will scour the internet for any clue about your identity. If they find the right information, they could wreak havoc on your finances.

Keep your personal details vague. It may seem harmless to post references to your age, your birthday, or where you were born, but these could be valuable clues for identity thieves.

Choose your friends wisely. Hackers commonly use fake social media profiles to try to scam people out of money or to steal their identity. Don't accept friend requests from people you don't know in real life.

Avoid sharing your location. While it may be exciting to post about your vacation, you could be unwittingly letting burglars know that you'll be out of your house for an extended period of time.

Social media websites are free to use, but they need to make money somehow. One way they do this is by selling advertising space on their websites. These catchy ads are often tailored to your personal interests and likes. Take a moment before you click. It's possible this is a dodgy ad placed by a scammer.

The Better Business Bureau (BBB) has received thousands of complaints about misleading Facebook and Instagram ads, including those claiming to support charities. Protect yourself by researching the business before making a purchase, searching the internet for complaints on the company or product, and verifying a charity at *Give.org* before donating.

Insider's guide to Facebook privacy

When Mark Zuckerberg launched Facebook back in 2003, it was little more than a platform for friends to share comments and photos. Two decades later, nearly 3 billion people around the world use the popular website to create social groups, organize events, sell items, and fundraise.

Because so many sensitive personal and financial details are tied up in your Facebook page, make sure your account is safe and secure. Here's how to use the settings to specify who can contact you and what info people can see when they view your profile.

1. Log in to Facebook at *facebook.com*. If you don't already have an account, create a new one with an email address.

2. Click or tap on your profile icon in the top right-hand corner of the toolbar. Select the *Settings & privacy* option.

3. Choose from one of these five options.

Settings. Within the list of many options here, you'll find *Privacy*. Click to change individual settings on more than a dozen tools. Check to see who can view your profile, who can send you a friend request, what data advertisers have access to, and more. This menu will also let you change any setting to be more — or less — strict.

Privacy Checkup. Here you'll find an easy-to-follow guide of Facebook's safety and security settings, all grouped by topic.

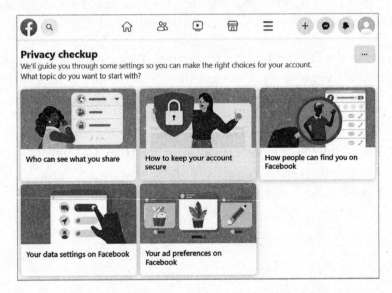

Privacy Center. This option gives more tips on keeping your account secure. It also offers safety and security info for other apps owned by Facebook's parent company, Meta.

Activity Log. Check out this overview of all your Facebook activity. See what posts you're tagged in, posts you have made, and more. If you notice any unusual activity, it could be a sign that your account is compromised. Change your password and go to *facebook.com/hacked* to secure the account.

Feed. Your Facebook Feed will display your friend's posts, news articles, videos, and other content. Use this menu to choose your favorite groups or topics to get news and updates. You can also temporarily "snooze" certain people or groups. This means you won't see posts from them for 30 days. If you want to completely stop seeing someone's posts without removing them from your friends list, you can unfollow them.

Get the big picture with Instagram

Instagram, owned by Facebook's parent company Meta, is a free online photo- and video-sharing app. It's another great social media platform allowing friends and family members to stay in touch.

Download the Instagram app from your device's app store or go online to *instagram.com*. Create a new account or log in using your Facebook account. Click on various icons to navigate and change your Instagram experience.

- From your home page, view your main feed of photos and videos posted by you and those you follow. You can like and comment on posts in your feed.

- Send private messages and photos to your friends and family members. If you linked your profile with Facebook, this icon may be different.

- Post a new photo or video to your profile page. Anyone who follows you will see this in their feed.

- Browse recommended posts. Instagram will suggest topics based on who you follow and what you've liked.

- View your notifications and activity, such as who has followed you recently or liked your posts.

- Search for topics or people to follow. On the website, this may be a search bar.

From the Instagram website, tap on your profile picture and select *Settings* to open the settings menu. Select *Privacy and security* to adjust your privacy options. A private account means that only your followers will be able to see your posts and activity. Use this menu to block accounts, limit who can comment on your posts, and more.

To access the settings menu from the app, go to your profile and tap on this icon in the top right. Go to the *Privacy* menu to adjust settings.

Create and inspire with the power of Pinterest

Pinterest is a social media site where users build virtual pinboards of images and videos. It's a great way to share cool ideas, hobbies, recipes, and more. Go to *pinterest.com* to create an online account or log in. You can also access your account through the app.

Use the top toolbar to navigate the site and create new posts. From right to left, this is what each button does.

- Return to your homepage.

- See activity and updates for the current day.

- Create new Pinterest boards or add items to existing ones.

To modify the privacy settings of your Pinterest profile, click or tap on the down arrow that is next to your profile icon at the top-right of the toolbar. Select *Settings* and click or tap on *Privacy and data*.

Want to get off social media for a bit? You don't need to completely delete your account. Most websites give you the option to temporarily deactivate or close it. Your profile will remain in digital hibernation until you decide to reactivate it. To do this, go to the Settings menu and search for *Delete* or *Deactivate your account*.

26 Texting

Think text messaging is just for the younger generation? Think again. This quick, convenient form of communication is popular with all ages. In fact, it's estimated that many adults over the age of 55 send and receive nearly 500 text messages every month.

These messages are sent between smartphone or cellphone users, usually through the phone's built-in texting app. But that's not the only way to stay in touch. Several third party apps let you send texts as long as you're connected to Wi-Fi. That means you can link your computer or tablet with your phone number and text from almost any device.

And now it's becoming common for texts to include more than a short written message. People can use their smartphones to share videos, emoji, photos, and more — all with the simple push of a button.

3 awesomely secure ways to text

Every smartphone comes equipped with a default messaging app. On iPhones and other Apple devices, this app is called Messages. Most Android phones use Google Messages, but some may come equipped with a different default app.

Usually, communicating is easy no matter the messaging app. However, sometimes iPhone and Android users will run into trouble when they're trying to text each other.

- Read receipts — which let you know if people have seen and opened your texts — often don't work across the two platforms.

- Pictures sent from Android phones to iPhones often appear blurry.

- Texts sent between iPhone and Android users are either Short Message Service (SMS) or Multimedia Messaging Service (MMS). Neither of these support the latest encryption technology, which means your texts aren't as secure.

Don't panic, though. You can still communicate safely, securely, and easily with anyone, no matter what phone they have. Simply use a third-party messaging app. They use mobile data or Wi-Fi to send texts, pictures, and more. Download any of these popular choices from your device's official app store.

WhatsApp. This is one of the most popular texting apps in the world. It's owned by Meta — Facebook's parent company — and it can be downloaded to Androids or iPhones. The app makes it easy to create group messages plus it supports video and voice calls.

Signal. This app boasts enhanced security features and robust encryption for every call and message. That makes it a great choice for people who are concerned about privacy and security.

Messenger. Facebook has a built-in messaging app that can also be downloaded to a phone or tablet. It's a great way to keep in touch with your friends and family who use Facebook, even when you're not at your computer. This app also lets you send videos, host large video meetings, and more.

Learn the lingo and text like a pro

Text messaging has evolved a style and language all its own. In the past, texts were expensive to send and you only had 160 characters per message. Plus it was a slow, clunky process on older cell-phones. To save space, money, and time, many texters adopted abbreviations and acronyms.

Even though modern phones have full-sized, virtual keyboards and no limits on texting, a lot of early texting slang is still in use. If you want to be a "text-pert," learn some common abbreviations.

- FYI (for your information)
- IMO (in my opinion)
- LMK (let me know)
- LOL (laugh out loud)
- JK (just kidding)
- NVM (never mind)
- OMW (on my way)
- TTYL (talk to you later)

If you come across any abbreviation you don't know, a quick web search should reveal its meaning.

Say more with emoji, pictures, and videos

A picture is worth a thousand words. When you're writing a text message, you may find it hard to put all your feelings and thoughts into just a phrase or two. Here's the good news.

Emoji. These small icons are used to express ideas or emotions. If you want to respond to a funny message, for instance, you might send a laughing emoji.

To add something similar to your message, tap this button on your keyboard.

Swipe left and right to view more options and categories. Tap the icons on the toolbar to quickly move between categories, or use the search bar to find a specific emoji.

Tap your selected emoji and it's automatically inserted into your message.

Pictures and videos. Texting is a great way to exchange photos and videos on your phone. First, tap on the + or arrow icon near the text box, or this icon on an iPhone.

This opens a toolbar that lets you view more options for adding content to messages. Find your photo library or gallery, tap on the photo or video you want to share, and click the Send button.

Because texting is so popular, scammers have flocked to their phones in an attempt to trick you out of your money. Stay safe by learning to spot these surefire signs of a texting scheme.

- Watch out for messages that promise free gifts, prizes, or coupons.

- Don't respond to text messages that say they've found a problem with one of your accounts. Many of these texts include fake links that harbor viruses or other nasty malware that will infect your phone.

- Be suspicious of any text from strangers that ask you to call or contact them regarding an unauthorized purchase or late payment.

If you suspect a message is a hoax, copy and forward it to 7726 (SPAM). This will help your mobile service provider filter out these messages in the future.

Make group texting a breeze

Most texting apps let you create group messages so you can have a conversation with several people at once. This is great for families, clubs, or social groups. However, they can quickly become overwhelming.

You may be inundated with dozens of off-topic texts, woken up at all hours of the night by incoming messages, or you may not even know everyone in the thread. Here are a few ways to make group messages a bit easier to navigate.

Keep messages on topic. When you send a text to a group message, every person in the thread will see it. If you have something to say to only one person, send them a separate, individual text.

Mind everyone's schedule. You may be in group messages with people all across the country, in different time zones. Or maybe someone in the thread is a late riser. Think carefully about what everyone could be doing before you text the group.

Don't be afraid to mute the thread — or leave it entirely. Turn your phone to silent or temporarily mute text notifications if you're getting too many messages. They'll be available to read later, so don't worry about responding right away. If you don't want to stay in the group, politely tell everyone you're removing yourself from the thread.

Chapter 27 — Video chats

Catching up in person with friends, family, or co-workers is not always an option. That's where video chatting comes in. This technology lets you see and talk with those far away in real time. Thanks to a powerful form of telecommunication, it's easy to send crystal-clear videos over home internet connections or mobile networks.

While video chatting has been around for decades, its popularity skyrocketed during the coronavirus pandemic. Millions of people turned to this tech to conduct work meetings, check in on family, or attend classes.

Now, you can choose from dozens of apps that make it a cinch to use your computer, tablet, or smartphone to connect with anyone, anywhere.

FaceTime — not just for Apple anymore

FaceTime is Apple's video chatting app. It comes pre-installed on Mac computers, iPhones, and iPads. Making a call to another Apple user is easy. All you have to do is click or tap on the app, press the *New FaceTime* button, and choose a contact.

In the past, only people with Apple devices could receive FaceTime calls. However, recent updates changed it so that Apple users can call anyone, regardless of which device they have.

Here's how to use FaceTime on an Apple device to call someone on a Windows computer or Android device.

1. Open the FaceTime app and select *Create Link*.

2. Choose how to send the invitation. For example, you can invite a contact via email.

3. A message with the FaceTime link will open. Select who you want to send the invite to and compose a short message.

4. The recipient will get an invitation link. When they click it, they'll be taken to an online page where they must enter their name, press the *Continue* button, and then press the *Join* button.

5. Once the recipient has accepted the invitation, you'll get a notification that they are waiting to join the call. Press the *Join* button to begin the video chat.

Remember, although now Windows and Android users can receive FaceTime calls, you need an Apple phone or computer to send out invites for FaceTime calls. If people with Windows computers or Android devices want to host a video chat, they must use a different app.

Connect virtually with the Zoom boom

Need an easy-to-use video chatting app that can host large groups and offers free calls up to 40 minutes long? Welcome to Zoom. Popular with business leaders as well as grandparents, this platform lets you connect securely for work or play.

Start by downloading the Zoom app to your phone or tablet from your device's linked app store. When you're ready to chat, follow these steps.

1. Open the Zoom app, and tap on the *New Meeting* button.

2. Select your settings for the Zoom meeting. If you turn on *Use Personal Meeting ID (PMI)*, participants will need to enter this number before they can join the meeting. Tap the *Start Meeting* button.

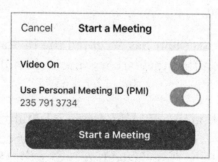

3. Your own video will be displayed. Tap the screen to view the toolbars if they are hidden. Select the *Participants* button to add people to the call.

4. Press the *Invite* button in the Participants window and choose how to invite people to the chat. You can send a text via the Message app or choose to send an email. Details about the Zoom call will go out.

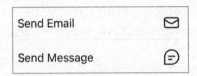

5. Anyone you invite will receive a text or email with a link that allows them to join the call. If they press the link, it will open Zoom on their device. However, if they do not have Zoom installed, they can connect to your call in their web browser. Depending on the call settings, your invitees may need to enter the Meeting ID or a passcode to join.

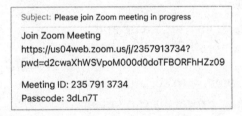

6. After someone accepts your invitation, you will be notified on Zoom. Click or tap the *Admit* button to let them in to the call.

Zoom is also available for desktop computers. Install it by going to *zoom.us/download#client_4meeting* and clicking on the *Download* button. You'll need to go through slightly different steps to start meetings and adjust settings.

No surprises: Booking a call is just mannerly

Zoom lets you schedule meetings and send out invitations in advance. That way everyone you want to chat with can plan ahead.

1. Open the Zoom app and click the *Schedule* button.

Schedule

2. The Schedule Meeting window will open.

3. Tap in the top text box to enter a name for the Zoom call.

4. Select *Starts* and set a date and time for the call.

5. Tap on *Duration* to set a time limit for the call. Free calls can last up to 40 minutes. If you run out of time, you can hang up and simply start another free call.

6. Select *Repeat* if you want to schedule a regular call. Choose how often you want the meeting to happen. It can be daily, weekly, biweekly, monthly, or even yearly.

7. After you've set up the meeting, tap *Save* in the top, right-hand corner of the screen.

8. Your scheduled meeting should appear under the *Meetings* tab in the app. Tap on it to view more details. Select the *Add invitees* button to share the meeting time, password, and other details with your contacts.

9. If you need to make changes to the meeting, tap *Edit* in the top, right-hand corner.

You can also schedule Zoom calls using your web browser or the computer version of Zoom. The process and menu options may be slightly different.

Catch up on-camera with 4 more chat choices

In addition to FaceTime and Zoom, you have a variety of video chatting apps to use for your next virtual hangout. Check out some of the most popular options.

Skype. Ever since this popular video chatting app was acquired by Microsoft in 2011, more focus has gone towards developing the communication and collaboration tool Microsoft Teams than advancing Skype. While certain business-focused features are being phased out, Skype remains available from all major app stores and online at *skype.com*.

WhatsApp. Best known for its text messaging features, this is a great choice for hosting video calls, as well. Download it to your mobile device or computer, then, to start a call, go to an existing text chat with someone and tap on the video camera icon. You'll send a video chat request to that contact.

Messenger. Facebook's Messenger feature also has a standalone app available on all the major app stores. This is a great choice if you already have a Facebook account.

You can also make video calls directly from the website by pressing the video camera icon at the top of a message window.

Google Meet. This replaces Google's old video chatting app, Duo. Meet comes pre-installed on many Android phones and tablets, but anyone with a Google account can use it to make calls. Download the app from your device's app store or go online to *meet.google.com*.

Finally, many social media sites — such as Instagram, Snapchat, and TikTok — have video chatting options integrated into their websites and mobile apps.

Nice to see you: Observe video chat etiquette

Don't let distractions or technical difficulties frustrate your next video call. Follow these simple rules so every connection goes as planned.

Keep your backgrounds simple. Many video chatting apps let you change your background — what others see behind you on screen. While it's fun to make it look like you're lounging on a tropical island or scaling a mountain instead of sitting in a clutter-filled living room, use these virtual backgrounds sparingly.

If the background is animated, too colorful, or makes it difficult to see you, it could be frustrating for other video chat participants. And don't change your background image during the call. This is equally distracting.

Practice before you connect. Make sure you have a good understanding of the app controls prior to starting the call. You want to be able to turn on your camera and microphone, adjust the volume, record, and more.

Mind the delay. There may be a lag in the audio during video chats, especially if someone's internet connection isn't great. Take a slight pause before you speak to make sure you're not talking over someone else.

Establish politeness protocol. Large group chats are a great way to catch up with friends and family members who can't get together in person. But if too many people talk at once, it becomes impossible to understand what's going on.

Some apps let you raise a virtual hand that appears on everyone's screen as a request to speak. No matter what system you choose, remember to be courteous and patient.

You must stay on top of digital security while using video chats. Follow these three tips to be safe even while talking with friends and family members.

- Keep your video chatting apps current. This will ensure you have all the latest security updates to help fend off viruses, hackers, and other online threats.

- Never accept a call from someone you don't know. Scammers have begun to use video chatting apps to con people out of their personal details or hard-earned savings. If you don't recognize an invite or call, simply ignore it.

- Mind the background when you're chatting. Even if you're talking to people you know and trust, it's best to make sure your video doesn't show anything in the background that might contain embarrassing information or sensitive financial details.

Top 10 Tips for Staying Connected

1. Don't open attachments or click on links in emails from people you don't know. Send these messages to your Junk Mail folder or simply delete them.

2. Unsubscribe from mailing lists and train your spam filter to help keep your email inbox under control.

3. Social media is great for sharing photos, news, and more with family and friends, but avoid sharing information that could help scammers steal your identity.

4. Don't share your location in real time on social media. You could be telling thieves when your home is sitting empty and unattended.

5. Get to know the privacy settings on your social media accounts. Make sure you place limits on who can see the pictures, status updates, and other details you put online.

6. Learn the acronyms and abbreviations used in text messages so you can understand what other people are saying.

7. Most devices come with a default text messaging app, but third-party apps are a good option, too.

8. Watch out for unsolicited text messages that promise free gifts or have suspicious links in them. They could be scams. Copy any suspicious texts and forward them to 7726 to help your mobile carrier filter out future spam texts.

9. Follow good video chat etiquette to make your calls smooth and enjoyable for everyone involved.

10. Make sure your video chat apps are up to date so you're protected from hackers and viruses.

Your Home

28 Better internet

The internet is vital to everyday living — to track investments, pay bills, read the latest news, stay connected with loved ones, and more.

Without a stable and fast internet connection, it's easy to feel like you're getting left behind. The good news? Getting online doesn't need to be complicated, frustrating, or expensive. With the right knowledge, you'll be browsing the web for less in no time.

Save your budget with 3 shopping secrets

Sifting through all the different internet providers can be confusing. Especially when you factor in their special offers that may include other services. Pick the wrong provider and it could wind up costing you hundreds of dollars every year. Don't miss the top things you can do to save money on internet, cable, and cellphone charges.

- The biggest mistake many customers make when they're shopping for a plan is assuming that bundling their cable, internet, and phone together will save them money. These all-inclusive packages claim to be convenient and cost-effective. After all, getting your services from the same company means you only have one bill to keep track of. And sometimes you can find great bargains. But bundling isn't a money-saver if you don't use everything you pay for — like that high-speed internet you don't need or those premium channels you don't watch. You may be able to find a better deal if you shop around and get these services separately.

- Avoid doubling up when shopping for services a la carte. For example, do you need a cable subscription when you already watch your favorite shows on Netflix? Are you using your landline and a cellphone or could you drop one? Read each contract carefully so you know exactly the services you'll be paying for.

- Already locked in to a provider? Try calling the cancellation department and say you want to cancel. They may offer you a better deal to stay. Just make sure you have another option lined up, in case they go ahead and end your service.

No need to change phone companies to ring up savings. Reduce your monthly cellphone bill with three key strategies.

- Sign up for automated payments or paperless billing. Because you're making your provider's job easier, they'll pass savings on to you.

- Use a limited data plan and dodge overage charges. Go to your settings and turn on automated notifications to be alerted when you're close to your data limit. While you're in your settings, turn off background app refresh so you're not using data when you don't need to. And use Wi-Fi whenever possible.

- Insurance may seem like a good investment to protect that pricey phone, but drop it to save $100 or more a year. Then set aside a few dollars each month to go toward a replacement if you need one. Protect your phone from damage with a sturdy phone case and screen protector, and you may not need a replacement at all.

Negotiate for a better deal

Paying for internet on a fixed income doesn't need to put a huge dent in your budget. Get a lightning quick connection at a price you can afford.

Research prices and compare your options online. Look for various offers but don't forget to check what's included with the service and the length of the contract.

Then contact different companies and ask them what deals they can give you, letting them know about other offers you've found. Don't necessarily accept their first proposal. If they're eager to get your business, they may lower the price or throw in free services.

Price break: You can surf and stream for less

Want to save hundreds on internet a year? The average high-speed plan costs nearly $60 every month. With a little know-how, you can cut your costs and still enjoy quick, reliable internet in your home.

Drum up senior deals. Senior discounts could help you save on high-speed internet, if you know where to look. Check out the Lifeline program from the Federal Communications Commission (FCC). It offers eligible seniors up to $9.25 a month toward their phone and internet bills. Go to *lifelinesupport.org* to see if you qualify.

Internet providers may offer you discounts, too. For example, AT&T's Access program offers similar discounts for certain customers who participate in the Supplemental Nutritional Assistance Program (SNAP) or receive Supplemental Security Income (SSI).

These deals vary depending on your location and carrier. Reach out to your internet company and research other providers in your area to see what options you have.

Slash your speed. You don't need a Lamborghini to drive to the corner market. Likewise, you don't need top-tier internet speeds to stream movies at home. So why are you paying for the premium package?

Internet companies pitch lightning fast internet hookups because they're also the most expensive packages. You might see ads promising blistering speeds of over 2 Gigabits per second. However, unless you plan on downloading a lot of files, you can opt for something cheaper.

Dropping your speed could save you a big chunk of change. Around 20 megabits per second (Mbps) is more than enough to stream movies, check your email, and surf the web without a hitch.

6 fast fixes to speed up your internet

You're streaming a show on your tablet or computer, and suddenly it starts to stutter and lag. Or worse — the internet cuts out all together. It's enough to drive you crazy.

You're not alone. A slow Wi-Fi signal is the number one complaint of home computer users. Fortunately, you might be able to fix a sluggish system yourself.

Turn everything off and on again. This tried-and-true fix could help reset your connection and make everything feel faster. Simply unplug your router and wait 30 seconds before you plug it back in again.

Move your router. Wi-Fi signal gets weaker the further you are from the source. If the connection has to travel through too many walls and doors, it could also slow everything down. Consider moving your router to a new spot in the house, if it's currently tucked away. You may also want to ask your internet company if they provide cheap — or even free — signal boosters that extend the range of your Wi-Fi.

Check the signal isn't overloaded. If too many people are using the internet at the same time, it can slow down the connection for everybody. Some routers let you prioritize certain devices, so you can ensure your computer, for instance, always has a quick connection.

Get on the right frequency. Most modern routers give you the option to connect to either a 2.4 gigahertz (GHz) or a 5 GHz Wi-Fi signal. You may see two separate names with these numbers when you try to connect to your Wi-Fi. And which one you use matters. A 2.4 GHz connection is slower, but is better at traveling through doors, walls, and other obstacles. While 5 GHz is lightning quick, you'll lose signal if you're too far away.

Watch out for signal thieves. Neighbors may piggyback onto your internet connection or hackers may hijack it altogether if your security is not up to par. All this extra traffic will slow down your signal. Use a strong password and a good firewall for your router. Consider moving your router to a new location in your home so the signal isn't accessible from outside the house.

Update your router. Older routers may not support the latest Wi-Fi technology and fastest internet speeds. So even if you have a high-speed internet connection, you may not be able to take advantage of it. Contact your internet provider and ask them to check if your current router is supported. If it's out of date, ask if they'll provide an upgraded one for free.

29 Home security

Your home should be a place where you feel safe. But if you're constantly worried about security, it's impossible for your house to become a sanctuary. For more peace of mind, turn to the tech world. Devices like alarms, security cameras, sensors, and smart locks could help protect you and your property from burglars and intruders.

DIY lockdown? 4 questions you must ask first

Many people opt for a professionally installed and monitored security system. That can be a good choice, but you'll spend a pretty penny — on equipment, installation charges, and monthly monitoring fees. If you're tech savvy, however, you may be able to set something up yourself for much less.

Smart home security systems are a great DIY option. They sync with your phone or tablet to help you create and respond to alerts. Many of them even let you add professional monitoring, so your system can notify the authorities or check in if you don't respond to the phone notifications or alarm. Get answers to these questions before choosing a smart system.

How much will extra equipment cost? Most DIY security systems come with a smart base station or hub — which serves as the keypad for your alarm — as well as a handful of motion detectors and sensors. However, you'll often need more equipment to cover your entire home. Take a look at the expense for additional sensors, cameras, and other hardware.

Will it work with other smart devices? Many security systems sync with other smart home devices. Some pair with smart video cameras, video doorbells, or smart locks so you can control all your security devices with ease. High-end systems may even automatically set the alarm when you lock your door. Find out if you can use your digital assistant — like Siri, Google Assistant, or Alexa — to arm and control your security system.

What is the backup plan? If your power goes out or your Wi-Fi isn't working, you don't want your house to be completely unguarded. Opt for a system that can connect to a cell signal so you'll still get alerts.

Are there hidden costs? Want to add professional monitoring? Or do you want your system to automatically upload security videos to the cloud? You'll probably need to buy a subscription plan for features like these.

I see you: Pick the perfect security camera

Outdoor cameras are a great way to keep an eye on everything around your home. But you'll find a dizzying array of options to choose from. Consider these features as you shop.

- Video resolution. You want to be able to see the security footage clearly, so opt for something that can record in high definition.

- Wi-Fi connectivity. Some devices can access your home Wi-Fi so you can check the camera from anywhere in the world.

- Video storage. You can choose a camera that records to a memory card or one that uploads the videos directly to the cloud. If you go with the latter, see how much cloud storage you can get for free, and consider the costs of adding more in case yours fills up quickly.

- Range of vision. Think about how much coverage you require from each camera. You may just need video surveillance on your front door, or you may want to be able to see your entire back yard.

- Warning sounds. Some security cameras can blare alarms or play a siren when they sense movement.

- Facial or motion recognition. Certain devices recognize and record when they detect human faces or motion.

- Weather resistance. Some security cameras aren't rated for outdoor use. Make sure to find one that can stand up to the elements in your neck of the woods.

- Night vision or flood lights. You want a camera that can record at all hours of the day and night. Choose one that can take high-quality video in the dark or a system with lights that come on when they detect motion.

- Two-way audio. Certain systems have built-in speakers so you can communicate with people you see in your cameras. This is a great way to give instructions to delivery drivers or scare off would-be burglars.

- Monitoring zones. Some cameras let you choose specific areas to watch for motion so you don't have to worry about false alarms. If the camera faces a busy street, for instance, you won't get an alert on your phone every time a car drives by.

- Power source. Battery-powered cameras are easy to place and are a snap to move around, but you'll have to remember to charge them. Cameras that need a cord may require professional installation or a visit from an electrician if you don't have an outlet nearby.

- Smart home integration. Some cameras can sync with your smartphone's digital assistant or other Wi-Fi devices. That allows you to use Siri or Alexa, for example, to control and monitor the security system.

- Cost. Decide how much you're willing to spend on a security camera. A less-expensive option may come with fewer features or less customer support.

After you've narrowed down the features you want, decide what kind of camera you'll go with. Here are your choices.

Security cameras. These offer a range of options and the flexibility to cover all angles of your house. Some companies even make less robust, indoor cameras so you can keep tabs on what's happening inside your home.

Video doorbells. These are a great choice if you want to be able to see who comes to your door when you're not at home or only need a little bit of video coverage.

Floodlight cameras. Want to combine motion-activated lights and a smart home security system? These are your best bet. However, they tend to be more expensive and difficult for a DIYer to install.

You don't want to spend time and money putting together a great home security system only to sabotage all your efforts by publicizing when your house is empty.

A huge mistake is announcing vacation or business trips on social media. A simple Facebook post saying "We're off to Florida in a week!" could tip off burglars in your area to the fact they have a window of opportunity despite your security measures.

Avoid posting photos while you're on vacation, too. Instead, wait until you return and make it clear you're sharing pictures from your trip now that you're back home.

How to protect your critical information

Part of staying safe and secure at home is preparing for natural disasters. Even if you keep your house stocked with canned food, bottled water, and other gear, you may not be as prepared as you think. Make sure your important documents are protected in case your home is damaged.

Safeguard vital documents. Keep these four things stored securely in a safe deposit box at your bank or credit union.

- An inventory of all the items in your home. You'll need this in case you have to file an insurance claim.

- Your car title. You rarely need access to this document, so it's perfect for a safe deposit box.

- Birth, marriage, and death certificates. The government will replace these if they're lost or stolen, but it's time-consuming and expensive.

- Your Social Security card. It can be disastrous if this gets lost or stolen. On the rare occasion you do need it, simply pick it up from your safe deposit box in advance.

Don't have a safe deposit box? Storing electronic copies of this paperwork on a secure cloud server could provide easy access no matter where you are when disaster strikes.

Keep these papers handy. Not all your important documents should be stowed away in a safe deposit box, especially since, upon your death, your bank will seal it until your will's executor can prove they legally have access to your accounts. It's imperative you keep these 12 documents at home in case you need to grab them when you evacuate.

- Your original will.

- A list of contact information for your employer, bank, insurance company, and utilities.

- Copies of both sides of each credit card.

- Copies of both sides of each family member's driver's license.

- A list of insurance companies with policy numbers.

- A list of banks and account numbers.

- Your passports.

- Personal checks and your latest bank statements.

- Social Security statements.

- Investment statements.

- Loan documents.

- Receipts for major purchases.

Smart devices are everywhere now. Companies have even begun selling internet-connected locks for your front door. On paper, these futuristic devices sound great. You'll never have to worry about forgetting your key because you're able to unlock your door with a fingerprint, your phone, or a passcode. Some even alert you when your door is opened or closed, so you'll know if anyone has broken in to your house. But is this fancy gadget a "smart" investment?

Smart locks can cost nearly $300. And while they come with fun features, experts say they don't do much to make your home safer. Unless you frequently forget your keys or want to be able to let people into your home when you're not around, the convenience of going keyless is probably not worth the price.

30 Smart-home technology

Adjust your home's thermostat from the car. Turn lights on with a voice command. Have the latest headlines read aloud while you're brushing your teeth. Does this sound like you're living with the Jetsons? No, you're living in a smart home.

Electronic gadgets that connect to the internet and each other allow you to use your voice, a smartphone, or a tablet to control and automate a variety of household appliances. These smart devices can transform your house into a safer, more energy-efficient smart home.

Are you listening? Smart speakers have superpowers

Smart speakers are one of the most basic components of a smart home. They come with a built-in digital assistant that responds to your voice, allowing you to perform a variety of tasks and control other smart devices. Once connected to your Wi-Fi network, all it takes is a "wake word" to get started.

This word or phrase instructs your smart speaker's digital assistant to listen to your instructions. It will vary depending on the brand. For example, you would say, "Alexa" to wake up Amazon's digital assistant. The Google Assistant responds to "OK Google" or "Hey Google." And Apple's HomePod responds to "Hey Siri."

Simply saying, "Tell me the weather" to your speaker won't make anything happen. But, if you say "Hey Siri, tell me the weather" or "Alexa, tell me the weather," your smart speaker will respond.

These devices are loaded with great features that make them excellent for older adults.

- Call for help or emergency services from anywhere in the house.

- Send text messages.

- Control other smart home devices such as thermostats, lights, and TVs.

- Set reminders for important events.

- Schedule appointments.

Because smart speakers are only part of a larger network of gadgets in your home, it's important to choose one that pairs well with your other devices. These are some of the most popular options.

Amazon Echo. Amazon's smart speaker — which uses the digital assistant Alexa — is the most common option. You can choose from the Echo, the Echo Dot, and the Echo Show. These devices represent over 70% of the smart speaker market in America. In order to use it, you'll need to set up an Amazon account and download the Amazon Alexa app to your smartphone or tablet.

Google Nest. These smart speakers are powered by Google Assistant, and can easily tap into the search engine's vast resources of information. They're a good choice if you own any of their other smart home devices, such as the Nest thermostat or Nest doorbell. You need the Google Home app to set up and customize this speaker.

Apple HomePod. While Apple doesn't offer as much functionality as other smart speakers, it's a smart choice for people who use iPhones or iPads. It pairs well with other Apple devices, and the high-quality speakers are great for music lovers.

The right senior-friendly tech gadgets can make life easier when caring for your dogs and cats. When looking for smart devices for pet owners, you'll find digital food and water dispensers, so you never have to worry about forgetting to feed your furry friends. And there are GPS locator collars to help you track your pets if they go missing. To keep an eye on Fido or Fluffy while you're not at home, install indoor security cameras as a great way to check in. Plus, they have the added bonus of making sure your house is safe and secure.

2 brilliant ways to light up your home

How would you like to turn your lights off and on from anywhere in the world? How about just from your favorite armchair? Smart lighting is another smart home component that can make your life more convenient and safer. You'll never have to walk into a dark room again. And it's a snap to schedule lights to turn off and on while you're away.

Most options are also voice-activated so you can control the lights with your voice, using smart speakers.

Smart light bulbs. These connect to your home's Wi-Fi or your phone's bluetooth signal allowing you to control your lights by name. After installing, you download the appropriate mobile app on your smartphone or tablet and pair each bulb. Certain systems require a central control bridge or hub in order to connect. Smart bulbs simply screw in just like regular bulbs, and while they can be expensive, they are more energy-efficient and last longer. Just remember, if you turn off the wall switch that sends power to these lights, the bulbs won't be able to connect to your app.

Smart light switches. Replace a traditional wall switch with a smart switch and you control the flow of power to specific areas and outlets. Just like smart bulbs, you manage these with a mobile app or a voice assistant. While more expensive than a single smart light bulb, smart switches are good choices for recessed lights, specialty fixtures, or large rooms. However, you may need to get the switches professionally installed.

Embrace energy savings with a smart thermostat

Heating and cooling your home is expensive. That's why you want to tweak the temperature based on the weather, the time of day, and whether or not anyone is home. Programmable thermostats have been around for a long time and can perform most of these functions. But spend a bit more on a smart thermostat and you'll have the capability to control your system with a mobile app, link it to your smart speaker for voice commands, automate multiple functions, and much more.

Take these things into consideration when shopping for a smart thermostat.

Compatibility. Not every heating and cooling system is compatible with every smart thermostat. Check that your system will work with a thermostat before you buy it. If you're not sure, ask an HVAC professional.

Installation. Many smart thermostats are easy to install and even walk you through the process with helpful apps and videos. However, some systems may require professional installation.

Sensors. You can prioritize which parts of your house are heated or cooled by pairing a thermostat with temperature sensors. Some systems even include sensors that will automatically turn off your air conditioning or heat if they detect a window or door is open for more than a few minutes. Check if these sensors cost extra.

Automatic temperature adjustments. Some smart thermostats let you program your own schedule. Others automatically create new schedules based on your previous temperature adjustments, when you're regularly in and out of the house, and the seasons.

Geofencing. This feature allows your smartphone to tell your thermostat when you're not at home. That way, your thermostat will automatically adjust the temperature so it's not running the AC or the heat while you're out and about.

Cost. Expect to pay anywhere from around $100 to well over $300 for a smart thermostat. However, some energy companies may offer deals or rebates.

Most new cars on the market come equipped with Apple CarPlay or Android Auto, allowing you to connect your smartphone to the car's infotainment system. The dash monitor will display a modified version of your phone's screen, usually with bigger app icons, edited menus, and a simpler interface. You can use your phone's GPS, listen to music, make and receive calls, send texts, and access other features while you're driving. Best of all, you use voice commands so your focus stays on the road.

If your car doesn't have this feature built-in, you don't need to spend thousands of dollars on a new vehicle. Aftermarket head units can let nearly any car sync with a smartphone. Some models even attach to your windshield with a suction cup so you don't have to pay for professional installation.

Chapter 31

Household productivity

Balance your budget, file your taxes, keep your home organized, shop for groceries — all those household responsibilities can easily fill up your days and weeks. But who wants to spend retirement bogged down by chores?

It's 21st century technology to the rescue. Believe it or not, you can use apps and websites to help simplify almost every household task.

3 easy ways to track your household expenses

Creating your household budget may not be exciting, but it's one of the most important financial tasks you need to do. A fundamental — yet tough — way to keep track of expenses is by crunching numbers on a spreadsheet. The good news? Your tech devices can make this job a little bit easier.

Preloaded spreadsheet apps. Most home computers come with productivity software and tools that make budgeting a breeze. Microsoft Excel and Apple Numbers can both be used to create a wide variety of spreadsheets. And they have prebuilt templates designed to help you keep track of your spending. The categories are already labeled, so all you need to do is plug in your income, desired spending, and actual costs to make sure you're on track.

Google Workspace. Want to be able to access your spreadsheets from almost any device? If you're always on the go, Google's Sheets as part of the Google Workspace is a great way to edit and track spreadsheets across multiple devices. You'll need a Google account to get started. Once you have one, simply go to *drive.google.com*, press the *New* button, and click on the small arrow next to *Google Sheets*.

If you want to edit these spreadsheets from your phone or tablet, go to your device's app store and download Google Sheets. Everything will be saved in the cloud, so any files you create or edit on your mobile device can be accessed from your computer. Plus you'll never have to worry about losing these files.

That's not all you can do with Google's productivity suite. Use Docs to create and edit text documents, Slides to make presentations and slideshows, and more. It's also easy to share any documents you have saved to your Google drive. Simply select the *Share* button and send your files to someone else. They'll be able to view the document and make changes.

Budgeting apps. Spreadsheets aren't the only way to make sure you're staying on budget. Many companies and banks offer budgeting apps designed to automatically keep track of your finances. Your device's main app store offers a range of different options to choose from. Consider these features to narrow down your choices.

- The ability to sync info across your accounts can help you keep track of your finances all in one place.

- Expense tracking helps you understand how much you're spending and what you're spending it on. Many apps identify different spending categories, like food, entertainment, and household expenses, so you get the best sense of where your money is going.

- Bill pay reminders will alert you so you never have to worry about missing a payment.

- Want to keep track of your budget with everyone in the house? Opt for an app that lets you share your budgets and spending with multiple people.

- While it seems odd to pay for a budgeting app, if it has all the features you need to keep you on track it may help you save in the long run. However, free apps are a good option if you're willing to sacrifice a few features.

Don't want to spend time on a spreadsheet or pay for a budgeting app? Simply search the web for free online budget calculators. These will help you get a good idea of how much you are spending, where you can save, and more. However, you won't be able to track your expenses in real time.

Go, go, Google — Workspace simplified

When using one of the Google Workspace apps, the process is similar to any standard word processing, spreadsheet, or presentation app.

- Create a new document by selecting one of the templates from the Template Gallery at the top of the Home page, or by clicking on the *Blank* option with the + button.

- At the top of the document window is a menu bar for managing and editing the current document. Click on the menu items to view the available options.

- Below the menu bar is a toolbar containing all of the main controls for entering, formatting, editing, and managing the content of your document.

- Anything you add to a document will be saved automatically.

Confused by taxes? Pick the best filing software

Doing your own taxes shouldn't mean laboring over paperwork and crunching numbers. Powerful programs can help you do all the heavy lifting. But what issues should you consider when choosing tax software?

Look for frequent updates. Tax laws change from year to year, so go for a program that will keep track of these changes for you.

Demand importability. Hate entering in all the numbers? Some software can automatically import information from digital files that you upload.

Consider customer support. If you're experiencing tech trouble or just have a question about your taxes, you may want to reach out for a bit of help. Some programs have real tax experts who will chat with you about your options. Others may only have computerized bots that can answer a few basic questions.

Check out their form library. Not every program has support for every single tax form. If you have complicated tax needs, opt for a program that has all the forms you need and covers all issues.

Decide what you're willing to pay. Many programs offer expensive packages that come loaded with features. However, there may be a free option available. If you meet certain income limits and other requirements, you may qualify for free guided tax preparation. For more information, go online to *https://www.irs.gov/filing/ free-file-do-your-federal-taxes-for-free*.

Cheap or free tax filing programs may lack certain features that would make doing your taxes easier. But don't pay through the nose to get the answers to nearly every tax question imaginable. Go online to *irs.gov/faqs* to view the IRS's Frequently Asked Questions. Use the search bar to find specific questions.

Stop dealing with paperwork forever

Ditch the paper piles and empty your file cabinets while still keeping every bit of important information at your fingertips. Sound impossible? It's not — if you have a smartphone or tablet and a scanning app.

Digitize almost any document by visiting your device's approved app store and downloading a free scanning app. Once installed, you use the built-in camera on your phone or tablet to create a digital copy of your document. When you're doing this, make sure you hold your phone or tablet directly over the paper that you're scanning so the information isn't distorted. Do it in a well-lit room so everything is easy to read.

Once you've scanned all your important paperwork, back up the files so you won't lose them if something happens to your device. Cloud services like iCloud, Google One, and Dropbox are a good option, but external hard drives work well, too. For more tips on backing up your data, see Chapter 23.

Once everything is scanned and backed up, you may want to get rid of some extra clutter. Use a paper shredder to dispose of old documents and financial records you don't need anymore. Just don't shred anything essential, like birth certificates, loan documents, property titles, and hard-to-replace financial documents.

Think it's impossible to beat the taxman? Think again. With a small investment of your time, you can totally eliminate your property taxes. The most surprising part? It's courtesy of your local government.

Some places allow seniors the opportunity to do volunteer work instead of paying a property tax bill. However, not all governments give you this option. Reach out to your city or county to see if they offer this program and if you're eligible for it.

Grocery apps check everything on your list

Many phones, tablets, and computers have note-taking apps built in. These are a great way to jot down a quick message, organize a to-do list, plan your holiday shopping, and keep track of household tasks. But if you're headed to the grocery store and want to make sure you don't forget anything, you may want to get a dedicated grocery shopping app. Here are some of the features that can make your trip to the supermarket a breeze.

- Hate darting back and forth through the store as you go down your shopping list? Some apps will automatically sort everything you add into categories like produce, spices, or canned goods.

- Consider an app that can sync across multiple devices. That way if you don't have your phone handy, you can add items to your shopping list with your tablet or computer.

- On a diet? Certain apps will let you view nutritional information about the foods on your list.

- If you're struggling to decide on a menu, some grocery apps will let you view recipes. When you find one you like, it will automatically add all the ingredients you need to your shopping list.

- Avid coupon clippers might want to choose a shopping app that tells which stores have the best prices and provides links to digital coupons.

- Check to see if your favorite supermarket has its own app that can help you organize coupons, track sales, manage your loyalty rewards, and even plan curbside pickup for your groceries.

Top 10 Tips for Your Home

1. Consider all the features you need when shopping for internet, cable, and phone service. You may find a bundle isn't actually the best deal.

2. Ask your internet provider about senior discounts or a down-graded speed to get a lower price on your monthly bill.

3. If you have a slow internet connection, try moving your Wi-Fi router to a new spot, turning your router off and on again, or asking for a free upgraded model.

4. A do-it-yourself, smart home security system could be a great way to protect your home without paying thousands for a professionally installed alarm.

5. Outdoor security cameras with high-resolution video, good night vision, and weather resistance can beef up your home's protection.

6. Smart speakers can help you stay in touch, call for assistance in an emergency, play music, or read you the news.

7. Some smart thermostats can go into power-saving mode when you're not home and over time learn your schedule to automatically adjust the temperature.

8. Built-in spreadsheet programs and budgeting apps are a great way to keep track of your household expenses.

9. Use a scanning app to create digital records of all your important documents so you can clear the clutter from your filing cabinet.

10. Get the most out of your grocery store trips by using dedicated apps to find coupons, look up recipes, and get nutritional information while you shop.

Health and Fitness

32 Health services

Access to a range of comprehensive health services is an essential part of your well-being. Over the years, technology has made these services more sophisticated and more available.

In the past, patients needed to visit doctors, dentists, or other health professionals in person. Now, websites, video consultations, patient portals, and other tools make it possible to get treatment from the comfort of your own home. These remote health services are great for people who live in isolated areas, have mobility issues, or struggle to find reliable transportation to health care providers.

In addition, telecare devices — which include alarms and sensors — allow health care professionals to monitor your health from a distance. If any problems are detected, they can alert medical providers.

The only requirement for online health care is a reliable, secure internet connection. You need to be able to talk to your doctor without worrying about your link freezing or hackers gaining access to sensitive medical and financial information.

Get health care from home

The wonderful world of technology means you can talk to a doctor online — so she can diagnose, monitor, and treat your health conditions remotely. This is sometimes called telemedicine. But if you need more, say the ability to communicate with nurses, pharmacists, and even social workers, then you're describing telehealth.

Think of it as telemedicine on steroids, because it encompasses a much broader range of services, including education, support, and preventive care.

Want to start using telehealth? Talk to your health care provider first, and ask these questions.

Do you currently offer telehealth services? Your doctor's office may have options that you want to take advantage of. If not, they could direct you to a reputable company or website.

What services can I get with telehealth? Some companies offer video consultations with doctors or nurses, mental health services, lab results, prescription management, physical therapy, and even health monitoring to help you track conditions like high blood pressure or diabetes.

How can I schedule an appointment? Most major telehealth providers have dedicated websites and apps that let you schedule a virtual visit or consultation. Some can even sync with digital voice assistants — like Siri, Google Assistant, and Alexa — so you can ask your smartphone or tablet to set up appointments for you.

What are the costs? Some telehealth platforms require monthly or annual fees. Check with your insurance company to see if any of the costs are covered.

5 tips for a successful virtual visit

Telehealth exploded during the COVID-19 pandemic. Now most experts agree it's here to stay, primarily because online tools make visiting the doctor easy, convenient, and — in many cases — cheaper. If you're new to this tech, make sure you take full advantage of virtual health care.

Prepare your virtual environment. Set up your computer, tablet, or smartphone in a quiet place. When you visit the doctor for a face-to-face appointment, you probably won't have to worry about background noise. But that's not true for virtual visits. Find a private, comfortable area where you can sit and talk to your doctor without interruptions.

Test out your tech ahead of time. You don't want to miss your meeting or not be able to communicate properly because your computer needs an update or your microphone is broken.

Come prepared with questions and concerns. This way you can make sure you cover everything and your doctor has all the info they need to treat you properly.

Document your visit. Take notes or record the meeting so you can review all the information when the call is over.

Loop in a trusted family member or friend. You may normally bring someone with you to the doctor's office to help you take notes or interpret information from your doctor. Ask if your tele-health visit can be a three-way call so that someone else can attend.

Harness the power of this critical tech tool

Want access to your health information 24/7? Then your doctor's patient portal will seem like a dream come true. Using this free online tool, you'll set up an account with a password and handle numerous personal health care tasks with only a few clicks of your mouse.

If you're not already signed up with your medical provider's patient portal, here are a few of the benefits.

- Make non-urgent appointments
- Refill prescriptions
- Request referrals
- Complete forms
- Scan your medical history

- Update insurance or contact information
- Check benefits
- Make payments
- Review test results
- Ask questions through secure email

Because patient portals contain sensitive medical information, it's essential you make sure they're as secure as possible. Ask your provider about their online security measures and steps they take to protect your data.

Don't let these senior programs go to waste

There's nothing wrong with asking for a little help — especially if you've already paid for it. Whether you're in a tight spot with taxes, transportation, medicine, or something else, let one of these senior benefit programs lend a hand.

BenefitsCheckUp. (*benefitscheckup.org*) This online tool connects older adults and people with disabilities to benefits their tax dollars have paid for. In fact, there could be 50 to 70 government programs for seniors in your state alone designed to help you save on prescriptions, rent, food, utilities, or even taxes.

Eldercare. (*eldercare.acl.gov*) As a public service of the U.S. Administration for Aging, Eldercare connects older Americans and their caregivers with dozens of helpful senior programs and trustworthy local support resources. Contact them if you need assistance with home care, transportation, or caregiver training and education. Enter your ZIP code or address in the box on the website's homepage to find out how you could benefit, or call 1-800-677-1116.

RxAssist. (*rxassist.org*) Visit their Patient Center to learn how pharmaceutical company programs and other resources provide free and low-cost prescription drugs. You'll find a searchable database of these patient assistance programs, as well as tools, news, and other ways to manage your medication costs.

Get the medical benefits you deserve

Making sense of Medicaid and Medicare can be tricky. But if you know where to look, you can find out exactly what benefits you're entitled to.

Medicaid. Whether or not you're able to get Medicaid hinges on where you live. Although the federal government partially funds the program, the states have a lot of control over eligibility.

Most of them use a formula based on income and family size. Generally, you may be eligible for some form of benefit if you earn less than 100% to 200% of the federal poverty level and are elderly, pregnant, disabled, a child, or a caretaker.

Almost every state has several Medicaid programs. And while all the states cover certain services — nursing home and hospital care, for example — dozens of other benefits are considered optional. Find out more about particular state programs at *medicaid.gov/state-overviews*.

Medicare. Are you passing up Medicare benefits? Only 1 out of 10 seniors take advantage of the free annual doctor's visit granted by Medicare Part B. Plus you're entitled to tests, procedures, and vaccines that will help prevent diseases. You can get yearly bone density tests, flu shots, and cancer screenings, to name a few.

For more information, go online to *medicare.gov/coverage* and search for procedures, medical equipment, and classes to see what is included.

10 terrific health websites for seniors

Want free health information and advice? Get all your questions answered from the world's largest collection of medical information. Simply visit any of these excellent websites and you'll essentially have access to the top health experts 24 hours a day.

- The Centers for Disease Control and Prevention (*cdc.gov*) is the leading science-based service organization in the U.S. designed to protect the public's health. Find information on diseases and conditions, infectious disease outbreaks, environmental health, and more.

- ConsumerMedSafety.org (*consumermedsafety.org*) is provided by the Institute for Safe Medication Practices (ISMP). Here you'll find out how to protect yourself and your loved ones from medication errors.

- Drugs.com (*drugs.com*) delivers a searchable list of drugs, an interaction checker, pill identifier, symptom checker, pricing guide, and more.

- The U.S. Food & Drug Administration (*fda.gov*) publishes the latest on the safety of drugs, biological products, medical devices, and the U.S. food supply.

- MyHealthfinder (*health.gov/myhealthfinder*), coordinated by the Office of Disease Prevention and Health Promotion, helps you understand medical checkups, screening tests, vaccines, and the elements of healthy living.

- MedlinePlus (*medlineplus.gov*) offers information on hundreds of health topics, drugs, supplements, and medical tests. You'll also find a hefty online medical encyclopedia and a catalog of healthy recipes.

- The National Institute on Aging (*nia.nih.gov*) has links to health topics, exercise, and healthy eating, as well as information on clinical trials, a catalog of consumer health publications, and topics specifically related to aging, such as caregiving and dementia.

- The National Institutes of Health (*nih.gov*) provides links to news, wellness toolkits, and more.

- The National Library of Medicine (*nlm.nih.gov*) is a gold mine of health news and research.

- WebMD (*webmd.com*) shares timely health news and in-depth reference material. They also present a symptom checker, information on drugs and supplements, and a search tool for local doctors.

33 Apps for disabilities

Smartphones and tablets are usually equipped with high-tech cameras, microphones, speakers, GPS units, and other powerful sensors and scanners. Many tech companies have started to put these gadgets to good use by designing apps to help people with disabilities interact more easily with the world around them.

Whether it's shopping or traveling, dining out or simply communicating with others, there's probably an app tailored to help you overcome accessibility barriers in everyday life.

To find and download these apps, search your device's linked app store — either Apple's App Store or Google Play.

Low vision? 3 ways your smartphone can help

Vision impairment is one of the top 10 disabilities among U.S. adults, affecting around 12 million people over 40. If you're blind or have low vision, you may face numerous challenges but thanks to modern technology, you don't have to feel left out of life.

Check out these smartphone apps designed to assist with daily activities, navigation, and more.

Get help with everyday tasks. Need an extra set of eyes when taking on chores? Here are two ways your phone can lend you a hand.

- Some apps connect you with sighted people who can assist those with low vision. Be My Eyes — which is available on Apple and Android devices — uses your smartphone camera to make a video call or send pictures to sighted volunteers.

They'll talk to you and, for instance, help with troubleshooting your computer or finding out if certain foods are past their sell-by date. Another app, Aira, is a live, on-demand productivity tool that connects you to professionals trained to assist those with limited vision. Double-check which apps are free and which require a fee to use their services.

- If you don't want to wait on a volunteer to help you decipher a label, consider an app that uses artificial intelligence to read text and recognize objects. These apps can access your smartphone's camera to read cooking instructions on packaged food, snippets of text on signs, and even describe objects and buildings around you. Apple users can download Seeing AI from the App Store and Android users can find Lookout on the Google Play Store.

Stay mobile and independent. Most smartphones come equipped with map apps that use your phone's built-in GPS to help you navigate in real time. They can even read out step-by-step directions for walking to the nearest restaurant, ATM machine, or park. Some have information on public transportation schedules and routes. Check if your city has its own dedicated public transit app that can help you find this information.

Other apps, like Nearby Explorer, have features specially designed for people with low vision. While using this, you can point your phone in any direction to hear about nearby stores, points of interest, and restaurants.

Zoom in for a closer look. A magnifying glass is a handy way to read small text or zero in on tiny objects. But chances are you don't always have one on hand. The good news? You can download free, easy-to-use apps that turn your phone's camera into a virtual magnifying glass. Simply search for "magnifier" on your app store.

Don't forget about features built into your smartphone that may help you see things a bit more clearly, like flashlights, screen contrast settings, filters, or different camera lenses. If your phone is lacking in these areas, search your app store for free options to download.

Your app store has dozens of options for dictation and text-to-speech apps. These let you use your voice to input notes on your smartphone or has your phone read aloud words on your screen. But think twice before you download them.

Your smartphone probably already has built-in accessibility features that let you turn text to audio or use your voice to control your device. For more information about these options, see Chapter 13.

Unless you want an app that lets you save your messages as audio files, has compatibility with e-books, or has other specific features, you may not need to spend any money.

Plot a friendly course with Google Maps

Imagine planning a trip somewhere new only to find there's no accessible parking or wheelchair-friendly entrances. People with physical disabilities experience this situation far too often.

However, with a little help from Google Maps, you can make sure your trips aren't fraught with these unexpected obstacles.

Streetview. Google has a small swarm of specially equipped camera cars that drive up and down streets, taking 360-degree photographs as they go. These images are uploaded to Google Maps and available to you when you select the Streetview feature. Check out cities, storefronts, neighborhoods, businesses, venues, and other areas you're interested in visiting. Check for accessible parking, wheelchair ramps, or any potential obstacles.

Accessible Places. Another way to see ahead of time if a business has wheelchair-friendly features is Google Map's Accessible Places feature. It will let you know if a business has wheelchair-accessible entrances, restrooms, elevators, and more. Here's how to turn it on.

1. Open the Google Maps app on your phone or tablet.

2. Tap your profile picture. Then select *Settings* and go to *Accessibility Settings*.

3. Turn on the *Accessible places* option.

Now when you search for a business or restaurant, you'll see a small wheelchair icon next to a result that is wheelchair-accessible. Tap on it to view a summary of the location's features.

Accessible routes. Using public transit with a wheelchair, walker, or mobility scooter can be tricky. Sometimes the most direct route involves flights of stairs or transferring between bus and train stations. But Google Maps can give you step-by-step directions using routes that have wheelchair-accessible features.

1. Open the Google Maps app and type your desired destination into the search bar.

2. Select where you want to go from the search results.

3. Tap *Directions* and then tap on *Transit* or the train icon.

4. Tap on *Options*.

5. Under Routes, tap *Wheelchair accessible* and then *Done*.

6. Choose your route and follow the directions to your destination.

Assistive apps make travel easier

Spaces unfriendly to wheelchairs, mobility scooters, and other medical equipment can present special challenges to your independence. You might face parking lots with narrow spaces, high curbs, and narrow doors — all barriers to smooth navigation.

With a little help from these smartphone apps, you can find stores, restaurants, transportation services, and other businesses that are accessible to anyone.

- Wheelmap allows users to collect and submit data about the places around them. That information is compiled to create a map of all the accessible venues in an area. You can even add pictures and comments about certain features or obstacles.

- Wheelmate has an interactive map that showcases the locations of accessible parking places and restrooms nearby.

- Rideshare apps like Uber and Lyft allow users to request a ride from cars designed to accommodate people using wheelchairs, walkers, or other assistive devices. Search for UberWAV or Lyft Access to find these features. Depending on where you live, certain options may not be available.

Your mobile device's official app store may have additional choices for wheelchair users and people with physical disabilities. Search for "wheelchair access" or a similar phrase to see what's available.

Whether you are visually impaired or simply need extra directional assistance at times, you'll be happy with Google Maps' Detailed voice guidance option. Turn this feature on and you'll hear more frequent and detailed voice directions when walking your chosen route. Hear how far away the next turn is, which direction you are walking, and if you are approaching an intersection.

Turn on Detailed voice guidance in three easy steps.

1. Open the Google Maps app on your device and tap on your profile picture or your account icon in the top-right corner.

2. Tap on *Settings* then *Navigation settings*.

3. Scroll down until you see *Walking options* and turn on *Detailed voice guidance*.

34 Tracking fitness

Setting fitness goals and keeping track of your workouts are the best ways to stay active and healthy. But it can be tough to monitor your progress or motivate yourself if you're trying to do it all alone.

That's where fitness trackers, smartwatches, mobile apps, and online workouts come in. A boost from easy-to-use tech can give you the incentive and the data you need to stay full of vim and vigor for years to come.

Get healthier with one simple device

Congratulations. You've made the decision to take better care of yourself. You're trying to eat right, take the stairs, and get the right amount of rest. But how can you tell if you're on the right path?

A fitness tracker might be just what the doctor ordered. These gadgets — which are sometimes called activity trackers or fitness bands — are worn on your wrist and keep tabs on your daily exercise and activity goals. See just some of the things you can do with a fitness tracker.

- Count your daily steps to measure the distance you walk or run in a day.

- Estimate the total calories that you burn.

- Log your food and beverages over the course of a day.

- Monitor your sleep for quantity and quality.

- Set reminders that encourage you to stand up and move around regularly.

Most basic fitness trackers — like the ones from FitBit and Garmin — are great for people who simply want to make sure they're staying active and healthy every day. You'll get plenty of features for less than $100. However, if you want more options, like the ability to download third-party apps or connect to a cell signal, you may want to consider spending a bit more on a smartwatch.

Tracker or smartwatch: Which is right for you?

Smartwatches — like fitness trackers — are an excellent way to keep tabs on your daily exercise goals and other activities. Both devices record workouts, count daily steps, monitor your heart rate, and give you daily wellness targets.

So why go for a smartwatch? It will have a bigger screen, a microphone, and a speaker. So it's really more like a tiny phone. That means it can pack in a lot more features than a fitness tracker. If it is compatible with your smartphone, you can sync the two, and all you need to do is look at your wrist to read text messages, answer calls, and even play voice messages. Plus some models can connect to a cell signal, so you can call for help or stream music even if you leave your phone at home.

Ask yourself these five questions and let the answers help you decide which wearable — a smartwatch or a fitness tracker — is right for you.

How much are you willing to spend? Smartwatches can cost significantly more than fitness trackers, but you'll get more features and options. Check out these examples.

- Smartwatches come equipped with digital voice assistance so you can control them with vocal commands.

- Pair a smartwatch with wireless headphones to stream music.

- You can customize the smartwatch display to make the info easier to read or just plain fun to look at.

- You have the ability to add third-party apps that let you use your watch to check social media, plan a walking route, and more.

Do you want a device that is compatible with your phone? Some smartwatches can only work with certain types of phones. For example, you may not be able to pair an Apple watch with an Android phone. On the other hand, most fitness trackers can work well with any mobile operating system.

Do you want to charge every day? Smartwatch batteries tend to only last a day or two, while fitness trackers can last for weeks on a single charge.

Is the device comfortable to wear? Fitness trackers tend to be lighter and smaller than smartwatches, so you may find them easier to wear all day and night. However, many smartwatches let you swap out the band for something comfier, while you don't have that option for many fitness trackers.

Is it easy to use? Different devices rely on touch screens, knobs, or physical buttons. Some fitness trackers have smaller displays or screens, which can make them tougher to use or read. Test out a few different models at your local computer store to see what you like best.

4 ways your smartphone can keep you fit

Think that spending too much time on your phone is bad for your health? Think again. With the right tools, your smartphone could actually be a genius way to keep track of your fitness. Check out these different types of apps that can help you stay active and healthy.

Pedometer apps. While most smartphones have a built-in tool to count your steps, third-party apps may offer different features, such as the ability to compare your activity with other users or the option to set daily goals.

Walking apps. These can measure distance, track the elevation changes, and record the route so you can repeat it. Plus, some apps let users share their favorite walks with others in the same area. Tap into one of these and you can explore new places while you exercise.

Calorie counters. Keeping track of everything you eat in a day is a breeze with the right tools. These apps will let you log your meals and automatically give you the nutritional information. Many counters also let you enter exercise regimens or workouts to estimate how many calories you burned that day.

Workout apps. Want to motivate yourself to get a bit more daily exercise? These apps can guide you through simple fitness sessions, encourage you to get moving, and track your progress. Look for workout apps targeted towards seniors to find exercises that are right for you.

Get with the program: Online workouts are here to stay

Does going to the gym make you anxious? Perhaps you can't afford a membership. No worries — there's an easier way to take part in a guided fitness plan.

Thanks to online workouts, you can get the benefits of instructor-led exercise without having to leave the comfort of home. These tech-enabled classes are super convenient and much less expensive than in-studio programs. Plus you can go at your own pace.

As you get started, consider the type of technology you want to use.

- If you have a Wi-Fi connection, you can stream videos 24/7 on your phone, tablet, computer, or television. Don't want to pay anything? Tap into free classes through YouTube.

- Some cable TV providers offer on-demand fitness videos. Many are free, but you'll have to foot the bill for others.

- Head over to your local library to choose from its array of exercise DVDs.

- Download exercise apps to your phone, tablet, or other electronic device. Just note, some require a paid subscription.

No matter which route you take, your options will appear limitless. So focus on what you want to achieve. These tips will also help you find an online class that works well for you.

- Find qualified teachers. Google your potential instructor's name to ensure they're certified in the fitness mode they're teaching.

- Look for a program with a variety of workouts. You don't want to focus too much on one set of muscles as it increases your risk of injury. Allow time for recovery between sessions.

- Consider your budget and workout space. You might want to look elsewhere if the class requires expensive equipment or large machinery you don't have.

Finally, check with your doctor before starting any fitness program to ensure none of your medications will make you dizzy while exercising. This is especially dangerous if you're home alone. If you're just beginning to exercise, start slowly and don't overdo it. Take a break if you feel pain or get short of breath.

35 Medical alert systems

Nearly 9 out of 10 seniors think it's important to be able to stay in their own homes as they age, according to the University of Michigan National Poll on Healthy Aging. But as you get older, chronic conditions and increased risks of falling make it harder and harder to stay independent. That's where medical alert systems come in.

Also known as life alert systems or personal emergency response systems, these provide fast access to medical assistance in the event of an emergency. That gives incredible peace of mind to older adults living alone, as well as their caregivers and loved ones.

Aging in place has never been easier or safer thanks to user-friendly tech devices like smartwatches, fall detector apps, movement sensors, and of course monitored alert systems. You'll find a variety of features and prices when shopping, so keep in mind your unique needs and budget.

Help at the push of a button? 7 deciding factors

If you live alone or care for someone with a medical condition, personal alert systems are a great way to make sure help is never far away. These devices are usually small, portable alarms that you can strap to your wrist or wear around your neck. When you push a button, they connect to a base station and call for help.

You'll find dozens of different alarm systems on the market, so don't waste your money on one that doesn't meet your needs.

Consider the features that will make you feel safe in your own home.

- Opt for something with built-in fall detection. These wearable alarms contain sensors that automatically recognize a fall and contact emergency services or your caregiver. Think about the range on these systems. You want to make sure it works even if you fall in your yard.

- Want to take your alarm on the go? Some systems have built-in GPS sensors so you can call for help if you experience an emergency while you're out and about.

- Professionally monitored systems are more expensive, but they let you talk to a person who can assess your situation and brief first responders if there's an emergency. Unmonitored systems can only dial preprogramed numbers — like a caregiver or 911 — after you push the button.

- Opt for a waterproof model. The kitchen and the bathroom are common spots for falls, so you want to make sure your alarm button works when you're washing dishes or using the tub.

- Some systems use cell signal to call for help, so your home must have good coverage. Systems that use landlines are cheaper, but that limits where you can install the base station. Alarms that connect to your home internet won't work if there's a power outage.

- Consider the usefulness and cost of extra accessories. Certain personal alert systems may let you add wall-mounted push buttons in areas with a higher risk of slips and falls, like bathrooms or at the bottom of staircases. Some companies may also provide a lock box with a key so emergency services can get into your home if you can't come to the door.

- Find out if you have to pay a monthly or annual fee to use the system, or if there are any activation and shipping charges. Check to see how much it costs to purchase the equipment plus any add-ons.

For reassurance when caring for someone with dementia or physical disabilities, don't miss these lifesaving sensors. Buy as a standalone purchase or add to a personal alert system.

- Bed sensors detect if someone falls out of bed or let you know when they get up in the morning.

- Door sensors send an alert when someone leaves the home. You can set it to trigger if the door is opened during a certain time period.

- Flood detectors, heat sensors, and smoke or gas alarms tip you off if someone accidentally leaves the stove on or the water running.

The smart device that can save your life

Wearable technology for seniors isn't just for fun. Certain smartwatches have built-in fall detection sensors that can automatically call for help when you're in trouble.

Apple Watch. When you initially set up your Apple Watch, you can choose to enter your age. If you tell it that you're over 55, Fall Detection is automatically turned on. Don't remember putting in your birthday or just want to check that it's turned on? Here's how.

1. Open the Settings app.

2. Scroll down and tap on *SOS*.

3. Tap on *Fall Detection*.

4. Tap the button next to *Fall Detection* to the on position. Tap *Always On* if you want your watch to continually be on the lookout for impacts and falls. If you tap next to *Only on during workouts*, the watch will be able to detect falls just when you start an activity in the Workout app.

When your watch detects a fall, a screen will appear on your watch that says *It looks like you've taken a hard fall.* If you haven't fallen, tap the *I'm OK* button. To call 911 right away, swipe the *emergency SOS* button to the right. If you don't respond, your Apple watch will call 911 after 30 seconds.

Android smartwatches. A handful of Android smartwatches can detect falls, but most can't automatically call 911. Instead, they'll send a message or call an emergency contact if they think you've fallen. If you have an Android watch with this feature, here's how to turn it on. The setup process may vary depending on your phone and which smartwatch you have.

1. Open the app you use to connect your watch to your phone. For example, if you have a Samsung smartwatch you will use the Galaxy Wearable app.

2. Search the Settings to find *Fall Detection* and toggle it to the on position.

3. Make sure you have your Emergency Contacts set up. If you do not already have any in your phone, you may be prompted to create a new entry.

4. When your watch detects a fall, it will send an SOS message with your location to your emergency contacts.

Want your phone to double as a fall detector without having to buy a smartwatch or other system? The main app stores have third-party apps that use your device's built in sensors to monitor for falls. If it determines you have fallen, it will call your emergency contact or 911. Just remember, you must have your phone on you for this app to work properly.

How to add medical info to your phone

Imagine you're unconscious and unable to speak to emergency medical personnel. How would they find out, for instance, if you're allergic to a medication or have a preexisting condition?

That's where your smartphone comes in. By typing in certain health information, you can help first responders, doctors, and nurses narrow down the possibilities of what might be wrong with you. And that means a quicker — and more successful — diagnosis and treatment. Plus, you can add emergency contacts so first responders will be able to reach out to your loved ones even if you can't tell them who to call.

Here's how to add the info to your iPhone.

1. Open the Health app and tap the *Summary* tab.

2. Tap your profile picture at the top right, then tap *Medical ID*.

3. Tap *Edit* in the upper right-hand corner. Turn on *Show When Locked*.

4. Enter your health information and emergency contacts and tap *Done*.

To ensure it worked, go to your Lock screen, tap *Emergency*, and click *Medical ID*. The information you entered should appear on your screen.

Got an Android phone? Input your data this way.

1. Open the Settings app and select *Safety and Emergency*.

2. Tap *Medical info*.

3. Enter your health information and emergency contacts and tap *Save*.

Medical personnel will be able to access this information even if your phone is locked, simply by tapping the *Emergency call* tab on the Home screen.

Chapter 36 | Monitoring health

Do you have a chronic condition or take multiple medications? Perhaps you're starting to feel uneasy, wondering if you must resort to expensive in-home care for assistance. Talk to your doctor and loved ones about taking advantage of modern technology before you make that decision.

If all you need is a simple way to keep an eye on your health and well-being, apps, smartphones, wearables, and other easy-to-use devices could be the answer you're looking for. They can help manage health problems, track your prescriptions and supplements, and more — all from the comfort of your own home.

Health check: 'Dr. Watch' will see you now

Smartwatches can sync with your phone to send text messages, answer calls, stream music, and even play games — all from your wrist. But you may be surprised to learn they can analyze a variety of fitness variables — see Chapter 34 for more info — and track vital health data, too. Consider these features when you're shopping for a smartwatch to audit your health.

- Heart rate monitoring. A small sensor detects your heart rate to let you know how hard your ticker is working. Some watches have the capability to perform an electrocardiogram (ECG) to look for irregular rhythm or other potential heart problems.

- Blood oxygen sensor. This keeps an eye on your body's blood oxygen level and alerts you if it's getting dangerously low.

- Blood pressure monitoring. Some watches use electrical sensors to give you this health info, but it's not always as accurate as the device used in your doctor's office.

- Sleep tracking. This can give you an idea of how long you slept, the time you spent in various stages of sleep, and how often you woke up during the night.

- Stress monitoring. This feature uses heart rate data and other skin sensors to gauge your stress levels. It suggests breathing exercises or relaxation techniques if they're too high.

Once you've narrowed down the features you want, start shopping for a smartwatch. Here are two popular options.

Apple Watch. This is one of the most popular smartwatches on the market, and for a good reason. It's packed with health-monitoring features, activity trackers, and fitness apps. However, if you don't have an Apple iPhone or iPad, you may not be able to access all these benefits.

Android smartwatch. A number of different companies create watches that are designed to sync with Android phones and tablets. The prices and features can vary greatly, so research your options carefully if you're shopping for one. Some of these can work well with any smartphone operating system, too.

While smartwatches are a great way to keep an eye on health information and monitor certain conditions, they shouldn't be relied upon exclusively. If you think you may be suffering from a significant medical incident or emergency, get in touch with your doctor right away.

Gadgets can help you stay well

There's no denying it. Rapid advances in technology have made it easier than ever to monitor and improve your health. Take note of these developments in the treatment of common conditions.

Asthma. People suffering from this chronic disorder can now be sure they're getting accurate amounts of medicine. Smart inhalers count drug dosages and track data about the time, date, and location of use. Such info can be used as a reminder to take the next scheduled dose, and may also help identify factors that trigger an asthma attack.

Diabetes. Wearable technology like continuous glucose monitoring systems combine sensors, transmitters, and a mobile app all in one package. These devices, which may come in small patches that adhere to your skin, can transmit real-time info on your blood sugar levels to your smartphone.

Epilepsy. People with this condition can fall and suffer injury during a seizure. But detection bracelets take notice of the rapid shaking that occurs during a convulsion and, when paired with a mobile device, alert caregivers with text messages and a phone call. Some even have GPS tracking devices.

Hearing loss. Some hearing aids can connect to phones and other devices that use Bluetooth, a technology that relies on short-wave radio frequency. What's so special about that? Hooking the devices together can improve the ability to hear amid background noise and eliminate feedback from microphones.

Poor nutrition. Many seniors find their appetite and thirst signals decrease with age. That can put you at risk for dehydration and unintended weight loss. So search the internet for nutrition apps. They can remind you when to drink water, give you tips on preparing healthy meals, and help you keep track of calories.

Never miss a dose with medication reminders

Sometimes keeping track of pills — whether they're yours or for a loved one — seems harder than juggling a dozen balls. But not anymore.

Thankfully, modern technology can make it easy to stay on schedule.

Smart pillboxes. When it's time to take your meds, these devices emit audio and visual cues to alert you. Generally, a one-button press is all you need to dispense your pills. But some models can be locked, which prevents access to the medication until the proper time.

Depending on the brand, you can get features that include personal voice prompts and caregiver notifications, including info on missed doses and low supplies. Some smart pillboxes require monthly subscriptions.

Phone apps. Some phones allow you to set medication reminders on them. If yours doesn't, you can download an app. Either way, just type in the name of your prescription and when you should take it. The app then sends a notification to your phone — a sound and a text message, for example — at the designated time. Swipe the screen to indicate whether or not you've taken your meds.

This software can also notify you of dangerous drug interactions, a helpful feature if you've got many prescriptions from different doctors. Some apps alert you when it's time for a refill and notify caregivers of missed doses.

Don't let blue light ruin your rest

If you're like the average American, you spend seven hours a day looking at computer and smartphone screens. Unfortunately, it's a practice that could be ruining your sleep. These devices give off blue light, which blocks your body's ability to produce melatonin.

Your body uses this natural chemical to tell your brain to go to sleep. So if you're using screens too close to bedtime, your brain never gets the signal to turn off for the day. Try to cut back on using your phone or looking at screens about three hours before bedtime.

Some devices also let you reduce the amount of blue light coming from the screen. On an iPhone or iPad, enable this mode by going to the Settings app and tapping on *Display & Brightness*. Select the *Night Shift* option to schedule when this mode turns on.

Android devices have a similar feature. Open the Settings app and select *Display*. Tap on *Eye Comfort Shield*. Select *Adaptive* to automatically turn on this feature based on the time of day, or create your own schedule with the *Custom* setting.

Sleep better with these high-tech gadgets

A poor night's rest isn't just unpleasant, it's bad for your health. Research shows that not getting enough sleep increases your risk of chronic conditions like diabetes, high blood pressure, and obesity. Tech devices may get the blame for keeping people awake all night long, but did you know there are plenty of devices and apps that actually help you sleep? Try them out to get a better night's rest.

Smart mattress pads. These thin sensors slip under your mattress and record data about your sleep cycles, snoring, and more. Some can sync with smart lights and thermostats to automatically dim the room and set an ideal sleeping temperature when you get in bed. Other smart mattresses and covers heat or cool your mattress, adjust the firmness, and track even more health data.

Sleep tracking apps. Do you keep your smartphone on your nightstand? If so, you may want to download an app to monitor your sleep. It can pinpoint any disturbances or health problems that are keeping you up.

Some can sync with a wearable device — like a smartwatch or a fitness tracker — to measure your breathing and heart rate to record your sleep cycles. Others use audio recordings or even sonar to measure how often you move around in the bed, whether or not you are snoring, and more.

Earbuds. You may not think more noise is the key to better rest, but some earbuds have features that may be just what you need. Maybe try ones specially designed to help you sleep by blocking out ambient noise — like traffic or a partner's snoring — but still play soothing sounds or allow you to hear your alarm.

Herbal supplements can be a great way to get a few more nutrients or soothe aches and pains. But before you use them, you need to make sure they're safe to take. Certain supplements may make your prescription drugs less effective or even cause harmful reactions.

Go online to *medlineplus.gov*, which is part of the National Library of Medicine, to find a wealth of information about herbal supplements, over-the-counter medications, and prescriptions. Click on the *Drugs & Supplements* tab on the top toolbar to browse products by name or use the search bar to track down your specific medication or supplement.

37 Personal safety

More than half of all Americans report being greatly concerned about crime and violence, with seniors feeling especially vulnerable. That fear can cause you to stop visiting friends and family members, cut back on your favorite activities, and experience an increased sense of isolation.

But you don't need to live with this anxiety. Let technology give you some extra peace of mind. Easy-to-use devices and apps make staying safe a simple matter.

Personal alarms: Safety on the run

Looking for a little extra security when you're away from home? Enter personal safety alarms. These are small electronic devices that emit a loud sound with the push of a button. They alert others to the fact you need help. Your well-being may depend on having the right kind, so use these tips to choose wisely.

Make sure it's loud enough. Look for an alarm that is rated at 120 decibels or more. For reference, the average human scream only reaches about 100 decibels. A louder siren not only makes sure you're heard, but it also means people farther away will know you need help.

Consider something discreet and lightweight. You may want to disguise your personal alarm as a car remote or a keychain. Look for something that is comfortable to carry around so you aren't tempted to leave it behind.

Check for a long battery life. Ideally, the batteries in these devices should last at least a year. Test it periodically to make sure that it is still working.

Think about extra features. Some personal alarms have small lights that flash to help people find you in the dark. Others may come with built-in GPS and the ability to sync with your phone, so they can automatically alert emergency services when you set off the alarm. These extra features are nice, but they will cost more.

Every older adult who lives alone needs to give friends, family, or caregivers a bit of peace of mind each day. It only takes a moment to let them know you're OK with a check-in app.

These smartphone apps send a notification at a scheduled time. You simply press the button to let your loved ones know you're doing well. If you don't, the app will alert your emergency contacts. Some even alert the police and request a wellness check if you don't respond to the notification.

You may need a subscription to access all of these features. To see your options, search for "Daily Check-in" in your smartphone's default app store.

Discover an app for every emergency

Your smartphone is likely within reach whenever you're out and about. That makes it a great way to call for help if you're in an uncomfortable — or even dangerous — situation. Adding the right types of personal safety apps to your phone could be just what you need.

Alert with a single tap. Some personal safety apps let you activate an SOS mode by tapping a button or using a voice command. The app will then send a message with your location to a preprogrammed contact, such as a friend, family member, or the authorities.

You may also be able to link the app with a personal safety alarm, smart pepper spray canister, or other device to share your location or call for emergency services.

Live stream your location. Some apps let you record and stream video and audio to your emergency contacts so they can see where you are and what is happening. Look for an app that also saves this video to a secure cloud server, so it can be reviewed later.

Fake call yourself. An ingenious way to escape an unpleasant situation is to look like you're busy talking to someone. Search for an app that lets you send a fake call to your own phone. Some also send a real call to alert emergency services without looking like you're dialing 911. It's a discreet way to get help.

Don't panic, call for help

You're in the middle of an emergency and need to call for assistance — but your phone has lock mode turned on for good security. Could you come up with the proper passcode in this frantic situation?

Fortunately, you don't have to. Most smartphones let you call for help right from the Lock screen. Here's how to make sure yours does just that.

Android smartphones. On most, pressing the power button five times sends it into Emergency SOS mode. A 5-second counter will begin. Once the timer ends, your phone can either call 911, share your info with emergency contacts, or start recording video.

1. Open the Settings app.

2. Tap *Safety & emergency* and select *Emergency SOS*.

3. Turn *Use Emergency SOS* to the on position.

4. Choose which actions will trigger when Emergency SOS is activated. You can enable any or all of these three modes. *Call emergency services* will dial the local emergency number. *Share info with emergency contacts* will send your location and an SOS message to your emergency contacts. *Record emergency video* will automatically start a recording to share with your emergency contacts.

iPhones. Tap the power button five times or hold down the side buttons to start an emergency call countdown. A timer will appear on your Lock screen. When it hits zero, your phone will automatically call 911.

1. Open the Settings app.

2. Select *Emergency SOS*.

3. Choose one or both of these options. *Call with Hold* enables emergency calling from your Lock screen by holding down the power button and one of the volume buttons until the *Emergency Call* slider appears. *Call with 5 Presses* allows you to call 911 from the Lock screen by pressing the power button five times.

If you need to add an emergency contact, tap *Set up Emergency Contacts in Health*. After your phone calls 911, your emergency contact will receive a text message with more information.

Never lose touch — for safety's sake

Every smartphone has a built-in GPS that tracks its location. This can be extremely helpful if someone you care for suffers from dementia and has a tendency to wander. Or maybe you are traveling and want family to be able to trace your whereabouts. And of course it's nice to keep tabs on young, first-time drivers as they go out alone.

Phones can share location data by using specially designed apps. Consider these features when choosing one.

- If you want to retrace someone's steps, look for an app that offers tracking history. You can see a map of where they've been over the past few hours.

- Opt for an app that sends an alert when someone travels outside their normal locations.

- Make sure the app works across platforms, especially if you all use different devices. Some locator apps are only available on iPhone or Android, so look for one that works with both operating systems.

- Consider an app that offers real-time location updates.

- Some let you access a few features for free, but others may charge you to use them. Shop around to see what fits your budget.

Some popular family locator options include Family360, Glympse, and Life360. Find these and others by searching for "Family Locator" on your device's app store.

You'll install the app on your device, sign in, then install it on your family's devices. Discuss it with all of the family members involved so they know what it is going to be used for and are comfortable with it.

Your TV, radio, and cellphone can keep you up to date in case of a disaster or accident in your community.

- Use your cellphone to monitor Wireless Emergency Alerts (WEAs), messages sent by the government to notify you about extreme weather or other emergencies in your area. You will receive these automatically on your phone, unless you've opted out.

- Stay tuned to local TV news for emergency information like boil water advisories and evacuation orders.

- Tune your weather radio to your local station so you'll get alerts all day, every day.

- Call FEMA for disaster assistance at 800-621-3362. The Disaster Distress Helpline, a crisis-support system for people experiencing emotional distress related to a natural or human-caused disaster, can be reached 24 hours a day at 800-985-5990.

10 deathbed secrets you shouldn't keep

If something were to happen to you, your online accounts could be locked forever unless you give someone access to your usernames and passwords.

Don't want to write them all down? Look into a password manager. These programs store all your login info in encrypted files. Make sure a friend or trusted relative can access your password manager in case of an emergency. For more info on choosing and using a password manager, see Chapter 16.

But that's not the only thing your loved ones should have when you're gone. Here are nine more pieces of info they will need to keep all your assets with the family.

1. The location of your will.

2. Banking and credit card information.

3. Investment account information.

4. The location of your safe deposit boxes.

5. Recurring bills that need to be paid or canceled.

6. Insurance policy documents, including policies from employers or organizations you belong to.

7. A list of houses, land, vehicles, and other major property you own.

8. Information about any business arrangements with others.

9. Your birth certificate, passport, and Social Security information.

38 Fitness games

Video games aren't just for couch potatoes. In fact, there's a whole category — known as exergaming — that combines video games and exercise. So how do they work?

Many of these games use advanced motion sensors to turn physical movements into virtual gameplay. Some may let you play while seated, simply moving your arms to control the game. Others could require you to stand up, kick, bend, tap your feet, stretch, or even dance.

The most common way to play these games is with a gaming console. Several options — like the Nintendo Switch — come with most of the equipment you'll need to start exergaming. Other major consoles — such as Microsoft's Xbox and Sony's PlayStation — may need additional accessories, like a motion-sensing controller, a virtual reality headset, or a motion-tracking camera. Certain games also come with balance boards or dance mats.

So jump on the exergaming bandwagon and have some fun while you get healthy and fit.

3 simple steps to choosing the perfect game

Ready to dip your toes into the world of video games? Use these top tips to get started.

Decide how you want to play. Some people love video games on dedicated consoles, like the Nintendo Switch or the Sony PlayStation.

However, these systems can be expensive, plus you still have to purchase games. To save some bucks, look at used consoles, or ask around to see if there's one you can try before you buy.

Another option is to use your smartphone, tablet, or computer to download games from your approved app store, either for free or a small fee. They may not be as elaborate or provide as immersive an experience as playing on a game console, but if you simply want interaction or motivation when you walk, run, dance, or work out, fitness game apps may be the ticket.

Just remember, there's a difference between straight up fitness apps — which merely track your data — and fitness games — where playing the game is the primary purpose, with exercise as a benefit.

Follow your interests. Once you've found a way to play, you need to find the right game for you. Maybe you want to start with games that reflect your hobbies, like bowling or tennis. On the other hand, this could be the perfect way to try out something new.

For a bit more guidance, talk to an employee at a local video game store. They can help you pick beginner-friendly games, or even let you test them out before making a purchase.

Ask your friends and family what they're playing. Reach out to your grandkids to see what they like. You could invite them over for a fun-filled Saturday afternoon of popcorn and video games. Do they live far away? No problem. Some games let you play online, so you can use them to connect with people across the globe.

Video games can be a great way to get fit while having fun, but be careful. Virtual reality headsets could cause dizziness or nausea. And certain games that require the use of balance boards, dance mats, or motion tracking cameras could be dangerous if you're unsteady on your feet. Talk to your doctor before you try any of these.

Keep your mind agile with 7 super brain games

It's scientifically proven that video games can not only get your body in shape, they can boost your memory and cognition. Download one or all of these onto your smartphone, tablet, or computer. Then start exercising your brain.

- NeuroNation. Picked as an Editors' Choice by the Google Play Store, this app starts with a few questions so it can map out the best experience for you. After an "assessment" round for practice, you may choose the pathfinder exercise or take a different route tailored to your specifications. You can play three games for free daily.

- WordBrain. At first, you might think WordBrain's tantalizing puzzles are child's play, but don't be fooled. These clever word puzzles start off easy and get harder.

- Tricky Test 2: Genius Brain. Like brain teasers? This app is full of clever questions that will keep you challenged, entertained, and amused.

- Brain It On. If you like shapes, look no further than this physics-inspired puzzle game. Play solo or with friends to solve each puzzle.

- Two Dots. Artists will love the minimalist design on this award-winning puzzle where you connect and match dots to master challenges.

- Jigsaw Puzzles Real. Play on the go. Choose from 2,400 photos ranging from novice to expert difficulty. Or create a jigsaw out of a photo from your own digital gallery.

- Move the Block: Slide Puzzle. Test your spatial reasoning skills by moving the red block through a maze of other blocks to get to the exit. Try to solve it without hints.

Top 10 Tips for Health and Fitness

1. Telehealth lets you get medical care without taking a trip to the doctor's office. Find a quiet place, test your equipment before virtual visits, and come prepared with questions and concerns to make the most of your online appointment.

2. The internet is one source of medical information, but you need to be careful. Stick to trusted websites.

3. Google Maps allows those with physical disabilities to plan trips and ensure that a destination has accessible parking, ramps, and other accommodations.

4. Fitness trackers and smartwatches are great ways to keep tabs on your exercise goals. Fitness trackers tend to be cheaper, but don't offer as many features as smartwatches.

5. Smartphone apps can monitor your sleep, calories, daily steps, and much more.

6. Find free online workouts so you can exercise from the comfort of your own home and save money on that pricey gym membership.

7. Many smartwatches have automatic fall detection features and will call your emergency contacts or 911 if you have an accident.

8. Add your medical background and emergency contacts to your smartphone so doctors, nurses, or first responders have easy access to lifesaving information in case of a crisis.

9. Daily check-in apps allow your loved ones to know that you are safe and well.

10. Exercising doesn't have to be boring. Some video games are a super way to have fun while you get fit.

Entertainment

39 Digital games

If you were into cutting-edge technology in the 1970s, you probably remember Pong. It was one of the first computer games ever created and is considered the granddaddy of the video game industry. Today you'll find digital games ranging from the very simple to the wildly elaborate. You can play on your phone, tablet, computer, or through a video gaming console. You can play by yourself, against a computer opponent, with other people in your living room, or via the internet versus gamers all over the world.

The term "digital game" can mean anything from a basic round of Solitaire to a huge interactive tournament played with multiple people online. Some games you buy and install on your device, some you download from your app store. Others exist only online.

You may be surprised to learn that more than half of seniors play digital games at least once every month. Want to get started? Gaming has never been easier.

Play it your way: Customize your gaming experience

Do you like playing chess or doing the daily crossword puzzle? As long as you have access to the internet, you can play dozens of board games, puzzles, and other games online. And the best part? Many are free.

Multiplayer games. You don't need to play electronic games alone. In fact, they're a great way to stay connected with friends and family members all over the world. And in some cases, you can even meet new people.

For example, Words with Friends is a multiplayer game where you take turns building words crossword-puzzle style in a manner similar to Scrabble. Play with a friend across the street or across the country.

Want more choices? Why not take a minute to browse Microsoft's MSN Game Zone at *zone.msn.com*. You'll find an entire multiplayer game category that includes backgammon, spades, hearts, and more.

To hunt down your favorite games that require two or more people, search the internet and join online versions, or search your app store for downloadable versions.

Single player games. Prefer to go solo? The internet has dozens of free puzzles and games that will keep your brain engaged. Check these out.

- *thejigsawpuzzles.com*. Go here for dozens of virtual jigsaw puzzles you can put together. Choose from easy 20-piece puzzles or complex 500-piece challenges.

- *nytimes.com/wordle*. You have five guesses to figure out the word of the day. The *New York Times* hosts other free-to-play word puzzles, like Spelling Bee and Letter Boxed.

- *sudoku.com*. Play this challenging number puzzle for free. If you're a beginner, select the *Easy* level at the top of the screen.

Budget-friendly tricks to get your game on

No need to spend hundreds of dollars on an expensive console or high-end computer to start playing video games. With a little know-how, you can find fun games for little — or no — cost.

Download free apps to your mobile device. The official app store for your smartphone or tablet has dozens of free games you can download and play. These are a great way to pass the time while you travel or when you simply want to relax at home.

Just watch out for those with in-app purchases. These can be ad-free upgrades to the paid version, features you pay for to unlock additional abilities or levels, special items for sale, and more. As optional charges, they basically allow the app developer to provide their app for free. But you're under no obligation to purchase any of these.

Don't buy the newest games and the latest tech. Brand new consoles can cost hundreds of dollars, and when games are released they can sell for $60 or more. But if you buy last-generation consoles and used games, you can play for a fraction of the price.

Be a savvy shopper. Many online stores — like Steam, the PlayStation Store, or the Nintendo eShop — have regular sales. You may be able to find some great bargains. And if you hunt around, you might even find games that are temporarily free to play.

Consider a subscription service. Apple Arcade and Google Play Club do require a small monthly fee, but if you subscribe you have a huge library of games you can download and play whenever you want. If you play on a console or a computer, other subscription services — such as Amazon's Prime Gaming or Microsoft Xbox's Game Pass — offer games that are included with your membership.

Online multiplayer games and apps are a great way to connect with people, but still be careful. Because players use aliases, you may never know exactly who you're communicating with.

Set up an account with a strong password. And your online alias shouldn't include your real name, your date of birth, or where you went to school. In general, avoid giving out any personal information or financial details.

40 Photos

People have taken more than 12 trillion photographs since the first picture was captured by French scientist Joseph Nicéphore Niépce in 1826. Astonishingly, close to 2 trillion of these were shot just last year.

The reason for the recent upswing? The rising popularity of smartphones means that almost everyone has a high-quality camera with them all the time. These devices take digital photos, which means they use electronic sensors to record images instead of film.

But even though you no longer have to worry about wasting film every time you take a photo, you still want to be able to take great pictures.

Luckily your smartphone has everything you need to snap high quality shots, edit them to perfection, and share them with all your loved ones.

Capture better shots on your smartphone

More than 40% of people claim that camera quality is the most important thing they consider when choosing a smartphone. And it's easy to see why. That perfect picture of your grandchild dancing in your kitchen will be useless if it's a dim, blurry mess. Want to make sure that every picture you take is great? Try these simple tips.

Use the gridlines to help you line up your shots. Professional photographers often use something called the rule of thirds to compose their pictures, where they use a grid with two horizontal lines and two vertical lines to divide the image into nine distinct segments. The main subject of the photo is positioned at one of the intersections of these lines, instead of right in the middle of the frame.

Most smartphone cameras let you turn on gridlines so you don't have to visualize these in your head.

- On an iPhone, go to the Settings app and tap on *Camera*. Find the *Grid* option and toggle it to the on position.

- On an Android, open the Camera app and select the Settings menu. Locate the *Gridlines* option and turn it to the on position.

Take advantage of great light. Ask any photographer and they'll tell you that good lighting is the key to a perfect picture. While most smartphones have a flash feature, they tend to produce harsh, washed-out photos.

Instead, use natural light or other ambient light from buildings. Be patient and wait for the sun or clouds to shift if you're taking pictures outside. And try shooting during the golden hour, which is the time shortly after dawn or right before dusk. When the sun is low in the sky it produces dazzling, warm light that makes photos pop.

Play with angles and perspectives. Smartphones can easily store thousands of pictures, so don't be stingy when you're snapping shots. Take pictures of scenes, landmarks, or objects from a few angles. And try rotating your phone between landscape and portrait mode.

Leave some space to tweak and crop. When taking pictures, keep in mind that editing them on a smartphone is a simple process. Leave a little bit of extra room around the edges of your photo so you can crop out background objects, straighten the picture, or zoom in on the subject.

Avoid zooming in too much unless you're trying to capture something super far away. Many smartphone cameras use a digital zoom, which means the more you zoom in, the grainier your final picture will appear.

Play with filters and effects. Smartphone cameras can apply filters to change the colors in your shots. Try playing with different options to see what you like best. If you don't like the way a photo looks with a filter, don't worry. You can remove many of these effects in an editing app.

6 easy ways to enhance your photos

Very few photos are perfect the moment they're taken. Even professional photographers edit their pictures to get them just right. If you want to give your iPhone photos that professional touch, these editing tips can help you take them to the next level.

To get started, open the Photos app and select the picture you want to tweak. Tap the *Edit* button in the top right-hand corner of the screen to access these tools.

- Tap this button on the bottom toolbar to adjust the light and colors in your photo. Swipe left and right to choose from options like exposure, highlights, contrast, brightness, and saturation. Drag the slider left or right to adjust each setting. Experiment with different options to see how they change the photo.

- Want the phone to do the heavy lifting? Tap this button to automatically edit the color and exposure of your photo. Tap it again to undo changes.

- Tap this button to view preset filters. Swipe from right to left to view the various options. Drag the slider left or right to change the intensity of the filter.

- Tap this button to crop and straighten your photo. Drag the border around the photo to crop it. Use the slider at the bottom to rotate the photo or to change the dimensions of the image.

- Tap the *Auto* button at the top of the screen to automatically straighten and crop the image. Tap it again to undo the cropping.

- In certain pictures of people or pets, you may notice that the flash causes the subject's eyes to glow red. If your iPhone detects red eyes in the picture, it will show this icon on the top of the screen. Select it and tap each eye to fix it.

Once you've finalized your edits, tap the *Done* button to save the changes. If you ever want to change them back, select the photo again and tap on *Revert* in the bottom right-hand corner. Your phone will automatically restore the photo back to the original.

Don't have an iPhone? The Gallery app on Android smartphones shares many of the same features.

Goodbye mess: Organize your cluttered pics

Modern smartphones can store thousands of pictures and videos. But if you just leave them sitting in your photos app, you may find it nearly impossible to locate your favorite memories. Use these tips and tricks to help you keep them organized and secure.

Create albums to store similar photos. Most photo apps let you add pictures to different virtual albums. It's a good idea to create some based on events, people, and places. Give each album a meaningful name so you can quickly find the photos you're looking for.

Clean out unwanted photos every so often. If you never delete pictures, you can quickly clog up your phone's storage with meaningless images or duplicates. Some photo apps have tools that let you find duplicate pictures and automatically delete them.

Back up your photos regularly. You don't want all your pictures and home videos to get lost if something happens to your phone, do you? Regularly upload them to an external hard drive or cloud storage. For more information on backing up your pictures, see Chapter 23.

Print portraits straight from your phone

Don't keep all of your photos stuck on your phone forever. Choose your favorites and get them printed.

Use a home printer. If you own a printer, you may be able to get top-notch photographs at home. Many modern printers have a photo mode or setting that enables them to create high-quality images. And they let you print pictures from your phone.

However, you'll probably need to buy special paper. Normal copier paper soaks up ink, which can cause the image to look fuzzy. Photo paper, on the other hand, has a glossy finish, which helps your pictures stay crisp.

Let an app do all the work. Don't want to bother with printing at home? Photo printing apps let you upload images to a third party from your smartphone or tablet. For a small fee, the images will be printed and delivered right to your doorstep. Some apps even let you create albums, calendars, holiday cards, and more.

Check out services like Shutterfly, Snapfish, and Printique Photos. Many apps also have their own website if you'd rather use your computer to upload images and order prints.

Head to the corner store. Need your photos fast? Many stores have photo kiosks where you can upload images from a smartphone and get them printed on-site. Some stores let you use a smartphone app or website to send in your pictures in advance, so you don't have to wait around while they print.

Share your favorite moments

Want to share photos with friends and family members across the globe? You don't need to mail them physical copies. Here's how to make sure they can see your captured memories in an instant.

- Use the built-in photos app on your smartphone. To send pictures in a text message or email, open your photos app and tap on the share button. It will look like this ⌃ on an iPhone and this ⤳ on an Android. Select a contact and choose which messaging or email app you want to use to send the pictures.

- Share entire albums. Some apps, like Apple's Photos, will allow you to share the contents of a digital album. You may need to go to your photos settings and turn on *Shared Albums* before you can create one.

- Post your favorite photos on social media. Websites like Facebook or Instagram are a great way to share pictures. Your friends and family can head over to your profile to view the pictures you've uploaded. However, you want to make sure your privacy settings won't let just anybody look at these pictures. For more information, see Chapter 25.

- Host your pictures on free dedicated photo sharing websites like *flickr.com* and *myalbum.com*. These sites let you create online albums complete with labels to show exactly who or what you're looking at. Send the links to your family and friends so they can browse through your pictures.

Have a box of old photos you want to post online or share with your loved ones? Scanning apps, like PhotoScan or Genius Scan, let you use your smartphone camera to create clear, crisp digital copies of your favorite pictures. Share them just like you would any other picture you took with your phone.

41 Reading

For some people, nothing beats the feeling of turning the crisp page of a hardback book. For others, nothing beats the convenience of being able to download and read a book from anywhere. Maybe that's why 30% of Americans have read an e-book in the past year. And the numbers are rising.

Accessing exciting titles is easier than ever. You can do it from your computer, smartphone, tablet, or e-reader. With a touch of a button, you have a slew of content to choose from — books, audiobooks, magazines, and more. Escape to a realm where romance reigns, renew your mind with a daily devotion, or cozy up to the latest thriller. The opportunities are endless.

E-readers take the strain out of digital discoveries

Tablets make for a convenient reading experience as you can use them for multiple tasks. Check your email, scroll through Facebook, then get back to that enthralling memoir. Some people, though, prefer e-readers — electronic devices designed explicitly for reading digital books and periodicals. They come with some perks over tablets.

- More comfortable for tired wrists. E-readers are lighter and smaller than most tablets and books, which makes them easier to hold for extended periods of time.

- Longer battery life. E-readers don't use large amounts of battery power. This means you can use them for several days, weeks, or months on one battery charge.

- Less eye strain. Since e-readers are made for displaying e-books, they use a technology that makes the text easier to read. Some have a glare-free display, so you can read even in direct sunlight, say, at the beach.

If you decide an e-reader is right for you, here are some of the most popular options.

Amazon Kindle. As the main player in the e-reader market, the Kindle now has a wide range of devices. This includes the original Kindle, the Kindle Paperwhite, and the Kindle Oasis. These differ in terms of screen size, battery life, and storage space, but they are all excellent e-reader options. Some versions are even waterproof, so you don't have to worry about using them near the pool when on vacation. And you can easily download books from Amazon's massive Kindle Store.

Kobo. This is another significant presence in the e-reader market, with several different models, including the Kobo Elipsa, the Kobo Libra, and the Kobo Nia. The easiest way to download books is straight from the *Discover* tab on your e-reader, or on the website at *kobo.com*. It has a giant catalog of options that are sure to suit your fancy.

Onyx. This company produces a hybrid device that serves as an e-reader and also a regular tablet. While it is a good option for reading e-books, it's more expensive than dedicated e-book readers. Since the device uses the Android operating system, you'll download your preferred e-book app from the Google Play Store.

Elevate your book club pick with these tips

Roughly 5 million Americans gather in living rooms, coffee shops, and virtual hangouts for one of the most treasured pastimes — the book club. And if you're seeing more and more e-readers on the scene, it's for a good reason. These devices offer handy features that can up your book club game. While each e-reader has its own look, you'll find similar functions in them all.

Change the format to make reading a breeze. Make your book easier to read without purchasing a new copy by changing your formatting. Tap the middle of the screen to access page controls, then select the text icon.

You can increase the font size and even switch to an easier-on-the-eyes font. This is also where you change the background color to improve contrast, and increase or decrease the screen brightness.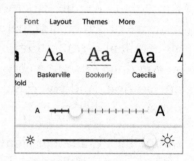

Bookmark pages so you never lose your way. When you're discussing the book of the month and want to refer back to a passage, you can always use the slider at the bottom of the page to navigate quickly. But if you save bookmarks while you read, you can use them later to jump back to specific parts of the book.

Tap the middle of the screen to access page controls, then tap the bookmark icon to save the current page.

To view your bookmarks, tap the bookmark menu icon. Then just select the one you want to jump to.

Take notes to shine during group discussions. Keep track of your thoughts and ideas by taking notes as you go. No need for a separate pen and paper, though. Just press and hold a word to select it and access its related controls. Tap the paper and pencil icon to add a note about the passage. Your notes will appear in the same place as bookmarks.

Selecting a word may also give you the option to highlight, look up the meaning of the term, or translate it. Drag the handles to increase the selected area.

Some e-readers have their own companion apps that you can use on other devices. For instance, if you download the Kindle app onto your tablet or smartphone, you can use it to access all of the titles that you have downloaded to your Kindle e-reader. This gives you the maximum flexibility in terms of how and when you want to read your e-books.

2 terrific ways to download books for free

Keen readers know the secrets to getting free e-books. Here are just a few of your options.

Free-Ebooks.net. With more than 40,000 titles in over 100 categories, this is a useful resource for any bookworm. You need to become a member at *free-ebooks.net* in order to access complimentary titles, but you can do this quickly with just an email address. Once you have become a member, you'll be able to download five free books every month.

Project Gutenberg. Named after Johannes Gutenberg, one of the first pioneers of printed books, Project Gutenberg is devoted to

giving online access to over 60,000 classic titles, which are free due to fact that their copyright has expired. Find this treasure trove at *gutenberg.org*, where you can look through the free offerings from authors like Mark Twain, Louisa May Alcott, and Charles Dickens. There is no registration required to download books from Project Gutenberg, and you can view them on a range of widely available e-readers or online directly from the website on a computer.

One of the main reasons customers say they are dissatisfied with an audiobook is because of poor narration. Luckily, most apps let you listen to a sample so you can check out the narration before you commit to buying the recording. The same applies for e-books. Before you waste your money on a shoddy selection, view the sample to see what you're getting into.

Enjoy bestsellers on the go

Nothing makes a long commute or plane ride go by faster than an audiobook. Listening to a classic or the latest bestseller is a welcome distraction and just plain fun. And you probably already have a compatible device that allows you to listen with ease. Smartphones, tablets, newer Kindle readers, and even Apple Watches let you get lost in a good read.

Get your feet wet with free trials. If you're an avid book reader, you may want to try an audiobook app that offers hundreds of thousands of books. These well-known apps are a good place to start. Some even offer free trials, so you save some cash while you decide which one works best for you.

- Audible. Amazon's provider of digital recordings offers two plan options. The subscriptions include unlimited access to thousands of audiobooks, podcasts, and more from the Audible Plus Catalog.

- Audiobooks.com. Similarly, this service offers access to an on-demand library as well as credits for free books from the premium store every month.

- Scribd. This service has been described as the Netflix for books. For a monthly fee, you get access to a catalog of audiobooks, magazines, and more.

- Google Play Books. This app is free to download, then you purchase audiobooks individually. It even has a free section with classics, self-help titles, romances, and more.

- Spotify. New to the game, this music streaming service has a catalog of audiobooks available for a one-time purchase.

Pay nothing for select audiobooks. If you are interested in the classics or little-known titles, check out these websites that offer free audio downloads. They're available for no cost because they're public domain books, but don't think that means you can't find excellent titles.

- *digitalbook.io*

- *librivox.org*

- *booksshouldbefree.com*

- *openculture.com/freeaudiobooks*

The perfect solution for small-print struggles

A gripping mystery novel. A sweeping romance. A thought-provoking biography. Whatever your taste in reading, you don't have to let failing eyesight deprive you of this great pleasure.

Your solution lies with the National Library Service's (NLS) That All May Read program.

If you have problems seeing a printed page, simply register with the NLS program and the library will send you free audiobooks and a digital machine to play them on. Getting a book is as easy as picking up the phone. You just call a number and request one. The library will mail the book right to your house, and sending it back is a snap.

To find a participating library in your area, call 888-657-7323 or go online to *loc.gov/nls* and click on *Find Your Library* at the top of the page. .

Save $325 a year on audiobooks. Sounds like a big promise, but the average U.S. adult listens to about 13 audiobooks year. At about $25 each, that adds up to hundreds of dollars annually. Save your cash by using your library.

Of course you can check out printed books and magazines, and audiobooks on tape and CD. But using the library app means you never have to actually travel to the library. Visit your library's website or give them a call to figure out which app you'll need to download. Libby, Hoopla, and Kanopy, for example, are popular library reading apps. Simply get your library card out and input the information into the app to digitally borrow audiobooks, ebooks, and magazines.

The only downside is that library systems have limited supplies of audiobooks. You may have to put books on hold and wait for them to be available. A small price to pay for free.

42 Streaming movies and TV

Back in the day, you never imagined you'd be able to turn on your TV or cellphone and watch your favorite movies and shows on demand. But these days, streaming media whenever you want — and often wherever you want — is a reality.

The term streaming refers to the delivery of digital content in a continuous flow over a wired or wireless internet connection. All you need is a compatible device, a reliable high-speed internet connection, and access to a streaming service.

Amazon Prime Video, Apple TV+, Disney+, Hulu, and Netflix are some of the biggest paid streaming services, but free options are plentiful. Either will give you access to large libraries of popular content, and some offer original content that won't be available through traditional cable and satellite TV. No wonder streaming has officially topped cable as the most popular way to watch television.

3 easy-peasy ways to start streaming today

The first thing you may picture when you think of TV streaming is someone watching shows on a smart TV that connects straight to the internet. That's a good option, but it's not the only one. You can access streaming services a number of ways.

Web browsers. It's easy to subscribe to streaming services and watch content through their websites when you're using a computer. Just pull up your favorite web browser, search for the name of the streaming service, and click on it to navigate to their website. For instance, if you want to subscribe to Apple TV+, you can do it at *tv.apple.com*. Many people find it easier to navigate web browsers on a computer compared to mobile apps.

Mobile apps. If you're using a smartphone or tablet, you may want to download the streaming service app onto your device. These apps are designed for smaller screens and offer special features that let you personalize your experience. Go to your device's app store to download the app. Then log in or create your account to get started.

Streaming devices. You can also access streaming service apps via sticks, dongles, and boxes that plug right into the back of your TV. They connect your television to the internet so you can sign up for, or sign in to, your preferred streaming service to watch your favorite shows and movies. The Amazon Fire TV Stick, Chromecast dongle, and Apple TV box are just a few examples. All of them have different interfaces but provide the same basic function — bringing you the entertainment you love.

Get the big picture: Send videos to your TV

Smart TVs and streaming devices deliver content from popular streaming services, but sometimes those just won't cut it. Maybe the content you want to watch is on an obscure video app that isn't compatible. Maybe you're watching movies with a friend, but they don't want to set up their streaming account on your TV.

Whatever the reason, you might think your only option is to crowd around a tiny device. But why watch streaming video on your computer or tablet screen when you could be watching it on the nice, big TV? Try one of these workarounds to display whatever you want on your TV screen.

Mirroring features. You may be able to mirror content from another device right to the telly. Just make sure your device and TV are connected to the same Wi-Fi network.

For Apple devices, go to the Control Center and tap the Screen Mirroring icon. Then select your Apple TV or AirPlay 2-compatible smart TV from the list.

The process for Androids will depend on your device and your TV capabilities. For example, some TVs support screen-sharing technology called Miracast. That means all you have to do is download the Miracast app from the Google Play Store on your device to get started.

Casting options. Similarly, you may also be able to stream videos to your TV from your device using a casting feature that sends just the video to the TV while letting you still use your device for other things. Within compatible videos on Apple devices, for instance, you can click the AirPlay icon and choose your TV from the list to cast the video right to the big screen.

On the other hand, some TVs have the casting technology Chromecast built in. So all you have to do is click the Cast icon within the compatible video on your device, then select your TV from the list.

HDMI cable. This option works even if you don't have a smart TV. Use it to connect your computer or other smart device to your television. Look for an HDMI cable that will work with your device. For instance, if you want to connect your iPad to your TV, you'll need an Apple-compatible HDMI cable.

Wireless display adapter. This device plugs into the HDMI port at the back of your TV. The adapter pairs with your device and lets you mirror whatever is on your smartphone, tablet, or laptop screen to the TV.

Forget monthly satellite or cable bills. Get a digital antenna. You'll pay once and be able to watch TV forever — including shows you'd never otherwise see. You can find one for less than a hundred bucks. Connect it to your TV and get access to all of the available digital TV channels in your area, for free.

Must-know features for successful streaming

Streaming services all have similar interfaces in terms of how you can access content on websites, apps, or TV screens. They'll look a bit different depending on the device and service, but learning how to use these main features can improve your streaming experience.

- Categories. The homepage of your streaming service website or app will display content by sorting it into categories. This includes popular shows and movies, original content, and also genres like romance and comedies. The items promoted at the top of the homepage change on a regular basis.

- Search. With the vast amount of content on streaming sites, it can sometimes be difficult to find exactly what you want to watch. Thankfully, streaming sites all have a search feature you can use to find categories of content, specific titles, or even available media that features certain actors.

- Live TV. Some streaming services have an option for watching live TV channels. This will vary depending on your location, but it can mean you don't have to switch from the streaming service to watch your regular TV shows.

- Watch list. When you're scrolling through the available movies and TV shows, you may see a few items you want to watch later. Add them to your watch list, so they're easy to find again. No searching, and no racking your brain trying to remember that movie you were so excited about last week.

The need for speed: Get fast-enough internet

One issue to consider when using a streaming service is the speed of your internet connection. This is important since you need the swift speeds to stream content continuously. A slow connection can result in jerky or freezing images.

In general, these are the minimum download speeds recommended.

- 3 megabits per second (Mbps) for standard video content

- 7 Mbps for High Definition (HD) videos

- 25 Mbps for 4K videos

Streaming services often offer different subscription plans, depending on the quality of video you want to access, with 4K usually being the best quality.

To check your internet speed, use a broadband speed checker website, like *speedtest.net* or *fast.com*. If the results are significantly different than the advertised speeds from your internet provider, contact them and ask them to rectify the problem.

Another issue to look into when using a streaming service is whether your internet contract is for unlimited broadband, or if there is a limit on the amount of content you can download or stream over the internet. If you don't have the unlimited option, you'll be charged for any overages. It may be worth the upgrade, particularly if you're planning to stream a lot of content.

Look for streaming subscriptions that allow you to cancel or change your plan at any time. Check out cheaper tiers and ad-supported options that can help you save a chunk of change.

Some streaming services offer an annual contract, rather than the more common monthly subscription. Paying yearly might be cost-effective if you want to commit to that length of time.

Here's the deal — nothing's better than free

One of the best ways to get a good deal on a streaming service is to take advantage of free trials. They usually last for seven days, but can be longer. Apple TV+, for example, offers a free three-month trial when you buy an eligible Apple device.

Free trials let you try out the service before you commit. Look on the websites of the major streaming services to see what free trials are on offer. With all of the options available these days, you could service hop for some time while enjoying your favorite TV shows and movies free. Just remember to cancel before the trial is up if you don't want to keep the service.

Buck up your budget with free viewing

Streaming means you stop paying for cable yet can still watch your favorite shows. Even better, when streaming is free you cut the cable and cut the cost at the same time. Use these free options to livestream what you want to watch, when you want to watch it.

- *crackle.com*

- *popcornflix.com*

- *therokuchannel.roku.com*

- *tubitv.com*

Free streaming services often have upgraded, paid tiers that come with more features. However, the free options offer a good range of content and they are an excellent way to start streaming movies and TV shows. You'll have to watch ads, but you can't beat that price tag. In some cases, the free services even provide live TV options.

If you use a cable service for watching movies and TV shows, a simple phone call could save you hundreds of dollars a year. This money-saving trick involves looking at your junk mail to find offers from other cable companies. Make a note of the best ones and then phone the cancellation department of your own cable provider.

Explain to them you have found a better deal and want to cancel your subscription. In a surprising number of cases, they will match the offer from the rival company and you'll get a lower rate on your monthly cable bill. But if not, you can always go ahead and cancel your subscription — and take the better offer.

43 Streaming music

You're just itching to hear that song you used to listen to on repeat, cruising down the highway in your first car. Or maybe you want to sway to the one you danced to at your wedding. You can listen to either instantly by streaming.

Streaming digital music is virtually the same as streaming movies or TV shows. You just need a streaming service, an internet connection, and a device like your smartphone, tablet, or computer. Then you can listen to songs on-demand from the service's catalog of music. That's millions of songs at your fingertips.

And it's more than a simple music collection. You'll have access to curated playlists featuring songs from certain genres, decades, and more. Plus some playlists are tailored toward your musical tastes, based on your listening history. It's a smorgasbord of sound for the modern music lover.

3 easy ways to get your groove on

Getting started with streaming is simple. Just choose an option based on how you like to jam to your favorite tunes.

Mobile device. All of the major streaming sites have mobile apps that you can download onto devices like smartphones and tablets. Then, voila, you can listen to your music on the go.

Head to the app store on your device, type the name of the streaming service into the search bar, and download the app. You'll create an account, log in, and have access to all of your favorite tracks, right there in your pocket.

TV. Convert your telly into a speaker by downloading the music streaming app onto your smart TV or TV streaming device. This option is great for when you throw a party or want to dance your way through a house-cleaning session.

Computer. Major streaming services also have web browser players and desktop apps. The interface looks a little different and may even have different features from the mobile app.

For example, if you use the free version of Spotify on a smartphone, you have to listen to playlists on shuffle. But the free desktop and web browser versions let you listen on-demand. A nice workaround.

Enjoy your favorite tunes for $0 a month

Many music streaming services offer free versions, though their features will be limited. For instance, you may have a smaller selection of songs to choose from, or only be allowed a certain number of skipped tracks per hour. And of course, you'll have to endure those ads.

Still, you may find that it's worth the savings. Check out these services that let you stream music for no charge.

Pandora. This service has evolved out of an internet radio streaming service, and offers free and paid options. With the free version, you create stations based on your favorite artists, songs, or genres. Pandora curates the music for you, and you teach it what you like by rating it thumbs up or thumbs down.

SoundCloud. This is a free music streaming service aimed at anyone who is interested in listening to the latest new music that's not necessarily widely available elsewhere. It's an excellent option for new artists to promote their music, but it doesn't have the same range of songs available on other streaming sites.

Spotify. As the world's largest music streaming service, Spotify has a huge library of songs and other content. Like the premium tier, the free version lets you create your own playlists, and recommends music based on your listening history. But you may not be able to listen to every song on-demand.

Tidal Free. The free version of the Tidal music streaming service has a large library of music with many genres and expert-curated playlists. The audio is lower quality than the subscription version, but it's still an excellent option for music aficionados.

YouTube Music. Owned by Google, YouTube Music specializes in audio and video tracks. The free and paid versions are a great option for those who also like to watch live performances and music videos.

Even if you're using a free service or experimenting with a free trial, streaming music can still cost you money. How? Data usage. You need an internet connection to stream music on your phone. And if you have a plan with limited cellular data, you may be charged if you go over. Here's what to do.

- Connect to Wi-Fi whenever possible. When you're on Wi-Fi, you don't use cellular data.

- Download songs on Wi-Fi, and listen offline. If this option is available with your streaming service, you can save your data and listen anywhere.

- Track data usage. Monitor your cellular data usage in your device's Settings app so you know if you're nearing the limit.

- Check settings. Some service apps offer features that lower data usage by showing fewer images and reducing audio quality.

Music lovers sing the praises of paid subscriptions

For dedicated music fans, a paid subscription to a music streaming service may have an avalanche of advantages over the free versions. You'll pay a monthly or annual fee for these kinds of perks.

- no ads

- on-demand songs with unlimited skips

- larger libraries of content

- download features that allow you to listen offline

- better audio quality

If that's music to your ears, one of these popular paid streaming services might be right for you.

Apple Music. With access to millions of songs in numerous categories, and completely ad-free, this is one of the most popular music streaming services out there. Listen to curated and personalized playlists, live radio, and more. Choose among subscription options for individuals, students, and families, which lets you and up to five other family members share access to those tunes.

Amazon Music Unlimited. Amazon Prime members get access to the Amazon Music library of over 100 million songs in shuffle mode as part of their Prime membership. They, as well as non-members, can get additional features, including the ability to play any song at any time, by upgrading to Amazon Music Unlimited. This also includes access to thousands of digital radio stations and Amazon's curated playlists.

Deezer. Another player in the music streaming environment, Deezer offers a mix of music, live radio, podcasts, and exclusive video with its subscription service.

Spotify. This service is particularly well known for its feature that lets users create their own playlists. Like other services, it has curated playlists based on genres, moods, and music you love. It also has a selection of podcasts, stand-up comedy, and language lessons.

Tidal. Known for its high-quality audio, the Tidal subscription service is a good option if you like the clearest sound for your music.

By now, you're familiar with headphones that connect wirelessly to your device using Bluetooth — no cords required. But have you heard the latest innovation in headphone technology?

Bone conduction headphones bypass your ear canal by relaying sound directly to your inner ear through vibrations on your head and jaw bones. They sit around your ear instead of in or on top, so you can still hear your surroundings. That's great for people who are hard of hearing.

On the downside, they're often more expensive, and some people complain about the sound quality. So no shame if you want to stick to the tried-and-true alternatives. Many folks say over-the-ear headphones are the most comfortable. Earbuds, which you insert into your ears, have the advantage of being small and unobtrusive.

No matter which kind you choose, make sure the volume is not too loud, as this could damage your hearing.

Look ma, no hands — smart speakers launch music effortlessly

Link your music streaming service to a smart speaker — a wireless speaker with a voice assistant built-in — and you can listen to music in your home without lifting a finger.

You'll set up the service in your smart speaker's companion app. For instance, to do this for the Amazon Echo smart speaker with Alexa digital voice assistant, you would just open the Amazon Alexa app on your device and follow these instructions.

1. Tap the *More* button on the bottom toolbar.

2. Select the *Skills & Games* option.

3. Using the magnifying glass, search for the name of your music streaming service. Tap to enable.

4. Sign in to your streaming service. Once it has been set up, ask your smart speaker to play tracks using voice commands.

Podcasts: A world of information in 1 convenient app

Don't know what a podcast is? That's because it's a made-up word — a blend of the portable media player "iPod" with the term "broadcast." Basically, podcasts are talk shows broadcasted online that you can download or stream with your device. They cover a huge range of topics. Gardening, true crime, politics, you name it.

Podcasts have become incredibly popular in recent years, and they're now widely available through music streaming services. Spotify, Apple Music, and Deezer, for example, have specific categories for podcasts, allowing you to access a number of shows. You can subscribe to individual programs so that you're notified when a new episode is released.

If you prefer to keep your music streaming and podcast listening separate, feel free to download an app just for podcasting. The Podcast app available on Apple devices, for instance, lets you search through a collection of millions of programs. Others are available for download from the Apple App Store or Google Play Store. Just enter "podcasts" into the search box.

Chapter

44 Home movies

In the not-too-distant past, capturing and displaying home movies was a long, convoluted process that required cumbersome equipment and a considerable amount of patience. But no more.

Smartphone cameras are not only great for taking photos, they also ease the stress of recording videos. What's more, once you have your video clips, you can edit and watch them right there on your smartphone, turning you into the next Steven Spielberg.

Smartphone videos in 4 simple steps

Odds are, your phone is never very far away. And that's great news when you're, say, playing with your grandkids and want to record their giggles and sweet smiles. All you have to do to capture the moment is pull out your phone and take a video. Here's how.

1. Open the Camera app on your smartphone. By default, this will be set to take a photo.

2. Swipe along the bar above the Shutter button until you get to Video mode.

   This is also where you'll find the modes for creating slow-motion or hyperlapse videos.

3. Tap the Shutter button to start recording a video. As the recording progresses, a timer shows the current duration of the video. Pinch your fingers together on the screen to zoom out. Spread your fingers apart to zoom in.

4. Tap the Shutter button again to stop the recording.

Once a video has been captured, it is available in the Photos app on Apple devices or the Gallery app on Androids. Open the app and tap on a video to view it. You'll see options to play and pause the video. Tap on the mute or unmute icon to turn the clip's sound off or on.

Need an even faster way to record videos so you don't miss a moment? To quickly open the Camera app, just swipe left on an Apple Lock screen or swipe left across the Camera icon on an Android Lock screen.

The default is set to Photo mode, but guess what? You can record videos without switching out of this mode. Just touch and hold the Shutter button to begin recording, and release the button when you're done.

On Apple devices, you can also press and hold the volume up or volume down button on the side of your device to record a video in Photo mode. If you're in Video mode on Apple or Android devices, you can still use the volume buttons to start and stop a recording. Just press and release instead of pressing and holding.

Lighting tips for the perfect at-home shoot

Good lighting is crucial for top-quality videos, but you don't have to invest in professional lighting equipment. Use these tips instead.

- Shoot videos outside to make use of natural light. The ideal time is early morning or in the evening. Both help you avoid the harsh midday sun.

- For inside lighting, try using any lamps you already have in your home. Big shades that diffuse the light are better than small ones that expose the bulbs. Keep the light eye-level, and avoid backlighting.

- Another way to improve the view is to use a selfie lamp, also known as a makeup lamp. These ring lamps create a flattering look when you're facing directly into the light. The ring balances the light across your face for a consistent, even effect. You can pick one up for about $20.

- If you wear glasses, look out for any reflections or glares caused by your lighting, as these can be distracting in the final video. Move your position or angle so that the light doesn't reflect off your lenses.

Shooting a video horizontally in landscape mode will make your video look more professional when viewed on a wide screen, like a television. On the other hand, recording the video vertically in portrait mode is best if you plan to post it on social media.

The quickest way to edit your clips

Editing your own home movies may seem like an intricate task, but it doesn't have to be. In fact, you can do some basic tweaks to your video clips right on your smartphone.

1. Open the Photos app on your Apple device or the Gallery app on your Android. Tap the video you want to edit.

2. In Photos, tap the *Edit* button. In Gallery, tap the Pencil icon.

3. You can press and drag the left and right edges of the clip to trim the video. This allows you to remove parts of the video at the beginning and the end of the clip, and is useful if there are pauses or gaps at these points. In the Photos app you can also adjust the lighting, add filters, and crop. If you have an Android phone, you add the filter before you record the video.

4. Tap on the *Done* or *Save* button to save your edited clip.

Give your videos the Hollywood treatment — for free

Sure, having video clips is nice, but if you want to combine them into a home movie collection, you can do that with video editing apps. These let you go beyond the built-in functions of your Photos or Gallery app. Look for features like these that will help your home movie shine.

*   Import video clips directly from your Photos or Gallery app, then combine them into one movie.

*   Link video clips together with transitions so one moves smoothly to the next. Transitions can be a simple black frame, or more animated effects such as dissolve and fade in or out.

*   Overlay text on the video for cool titles and captions.

*   Create background music, or use voiceovers to add your own sound commentary to a video.

All this Hollywood razzle-dazzle doesn't have to cost a thing. Just search your app store for free video editing apps like these.

iMovie. This is Apple's video editing app, and it's excellent for editing clips on an iPhone or an iPad. It has all the basics so you can create professional looking videos without getting a degree in film production.

VivaVideo. This is just one of the quality video editing apps available for both Android and Apple devices. It has a good range of features and fun effects, which makes it ideal for creating videos for social media.

Movie magic: Share videos like a pro

Now that you have wonderful home movies, of course you're going to want to share them.

You can do this directly from the Photos or Gallery app by opening the video and tapping the *Share* button. Then just select how you want to share the video by tapping one of the displayed options.

- Choose the text or email icon, for example, and your phone will automatically create a new message with the video attached. Type in the name of the recipient, and it's ready to send.

- Select a social media app for a quick and easy way to post to, say, Facebook or Pinterest.

- You may even have the option to cast the video to your TV by tapping the appropriate icon. Popular casting options include Apple's AirPlay or Samsung's Show on TV. See Chapter 42 for more details about streaming your videos on the big screen.

45

Smart TVs

What's the secret of the smart TV's high IQ? Its ability to connect to the internet. This feature is built-in, so all you have to do is follow the instructions to link the television to your home Wi-Fi router during the initial setup process. Then voila, you have a range of online options not available on a regular TV.

Like smartphones and tablets, these TVs let you access a range of apps. Which means all your favorite entertainment just moved to the big screen. Streaming videos and listening to music are a given, but depending on your TV, you may also be able to play games, check social media, control smart home devices, and more.

Learning the ins and outs of how to work your television is easier than you think. Familiarize yourself with a few key functions and you'll understand everything you need to know to get started with your smart TV, without all the tech frustration.

Plug and play: Smart streaming starts now

Streaming services are an increasingly popular way to access a wide range of movies and TV shows. And you can do this directly through your smart TV, without any additional equipment such as a streaming box or a stick.

In many cases, apps for all of the major streaming services — such as Amazon Prime Video, Apple TV+, Disney+, and Netflix — will already be prominently displayed on the screen of your smart TV. You can subscribe directly to your favorite by opening the app, signing in, and completing the registration process. It's that easy.

Free streaming services are even more effortless. Just download the app from the TV's app store if it's not already displayed, open it, and start streaming.

Of course if you want to watch television the old-fashioned way through an antenna or cable service, you have the best of both worlds. Nearly all smart TVs work with indoor or outdoor TV antennas so you can access local channels. And HDMI ports let you hook up your cable or satellite box to your smart TV the usual way.

Surf the web from your sofa

Use apps on your smart TV the same way you might use them on a tablet or a smartphone. The range of available options is more limited, but here's one you're sure to love — a web browser app. An increasing number of smart TVs come with one pre-installed.

That means you can access the internet and surf the web much like you already do on your desktop computer or laptop. It works similar to common browsers such as Firefox and Chrome, and may be titled something like "Web browser" or "Internet browser."

Just open the web browser app, enter a website address, and off you go. The downside is that navigating the on-screen keyboard with your remote control can be a hassle. But these tips will make searching a breeze.

Hook up your keyboard and mouse. Link a keyboard and mouse to your smart TV to create an experience similar to using a computer. Plug them into the smart TV's USB port, or connect wirelessly using Bluetooth.

Use voice search. Most smart TV remotes let you navigate with just your voice. Look for a microphone icon. Simply press the button and say the command. For instance, you can ask it to pull up a specific TV show, get the weather forecast from a weather app, or access a website through the web browser.

Since smart TVs are connected to the internet, significant amounts of data can be gathered about your browsing and viewing habits. To limit this, go to the smart TV's privacy settings and turn off personalization and advertising features. Make sure you're opted out of automated content recognition (ACR), which enables the TV to track everything you are watching.

Flat and happy: A guide to keeping your TV fit

Want to expand the life of your smart TV? The following info will help keep it humming along for years to come.

- Switch your TV off now and again. Just like pretty much anything else, constant use will wear out your television. So turn it off if you're about to fall asleep or aren't watching.

- Use a surge protector to defend against voltage spikes.

- Avoid overheating. Most TVs have their ventilation system behind the screen, so keep at least 4 inches of distance between the back of your television and the wall.

- Never clean the screen with chemicals. Instead, wipe it down with a dry rag or duster after turning the TV off.

- Keep the contrast setting at a reasonable level. A higher contrast requires more energy, which cuts into the longevity of your television.

Top 10 Tips for Entertainment

1. Digital games are an excellent way to keep your mind alert. Plus they're great fun. Check out the free options in your device's app store.

2. Use your smartphone camera for all of your modern photography needs. Once the photos have been captured, you can share them right from your phone.

3. A few taps of a photo editing app can dramatically transform your photos. Shoot them in landscape and portrait mode to give yourself the maximum flexibility.

4. Use the formatting features on e-readers and tablets to make books easier to read. Change the font style and size as well as the background to suit your needs.

5. Download samples of e-books and audiobooks before you buy the full version to get an idea of whether you are going to like them or not.

6. Cut the cable and start streaming movies and TV shows instead. For a bargain, check out some of the free streaming services.

7. See if your streaming service has an annual subscription option since it's usually cheaper than paying monthly.

8. Keep an eye on your cellular data usage when streaming music on your phone. To avoid data overage charges, connect and stream using Wi-Fi whenever possible.

9. Use a video editing app to add the "wow factor" to your home movies recorded on a smartphone or tablet.

10. Smart TVs give you access to shows and movies without the need for cable service. Navigate yours more easily by using the voice search feature on your remote.

Daily Living

46 Apps and app stores

Apps — short for applications — used to be called computer programs. But once mobile devices took the world by storm, the term expanded to include the individual, specific pieces of software available to download onto them. Think calculators, games, email clients, and more.

Every computer, phone, tablet, and smart device comes with certain apps preloaded. But with more than 7 million apps available worldwide, you'll find one to fulfill every need. Many are free. Some you must pay for.

You can use apps to learn, shop, play games, exercise, date, post pictures, watch videos, write letters, read books, order groceries, and more.

Although apps cover a huge range of functionality, they look generally the same on the screen of your device — small graphic icons. But once opened, each app will appear and act differently based on your device and the app's purpose.

Your easy guide to app-happy shopping

If you need shoes, you go to a shoe store. If you want a new app, it's only logical you should go to an app store. These are located online and linked to all of the major computing devices.

Shopping for an app is similar to any other shopping experience, really. You go to the store. You browse for the item you want. You find out more about the item. You make your purchase. Since many apps are free, this little exercise may not even cost you a dime.

The major app stores all have a similar format. Discover how to get to the correct store for your device.

Microsoft Store. This is the app store to visit if you use the Windows operating system on your desktop or laptop computer.

1. Click on this icon on the bottom Taskbar or from the Start menu.

2. Navigate within the Microsoft Store using the left-hand sidebar.

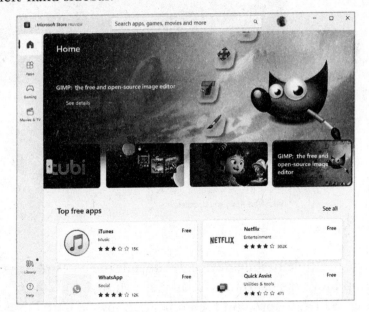

3. Enter a word or phrase in the *Search apps, games, movies and more* box at the top of the Microsoft Store window to look for specific items.

Apple App Store. Go here for apps, regardless of which Apple device you use. You may notice, though, the store's interface on a Mac computer is different from that on an iPad or iPhone.

1. The store icon will be on your Dock or your mobile device's Home screen. If the icon has a small numbered label on it, this indicates there are updates for some of your existing apps.

2. On a Mac computer, the left-hand sidebar contains the navigation for the App Store, with selected items appearing in the main window. Use the Search box at the top of the left-hand sidebar to look for specific apps.

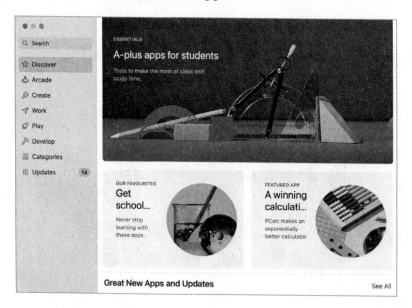

3. On an Apple mobile device, by default the App Store opens to the Today page, showing the latest apps and recommendations. Tap the magnifying glass icon to search.

Google Play Store. Find apps for Android tablets and smartphones from this icon on the Home screen of your device. See Chapter 8 for details about using the Google Play Store.

Each app has unique properties you may want or need to adjust. For instance, some require you set up a password. Others allow you to choose notification sounds, font size, a default shipping address, or profile picture.

Generally, you access an app's settings by clicking or tapping on a gear icon.

Jim-dandy downloads at your fingertips

Ready to jump into the wonderful world of apps? Start by finding one in your app store you want to download to your device. Click or tap on it to view some details.

Here you'll find the latest updates and reviews, as well as instructions for downloading. Click or tap on the relevant button — *Get* for the Microsoft Store and the Apple App Store or *Install* for the Google Play Store.

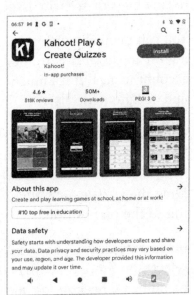

Once an app is downloaded, you can open it immediately by clicking or tapping on the *Open* button in the app store. Or go to your device's Home screen and locate the app's icon.

> Be aware of in-app purchases. You pay for additional content, extra features, or to use the app without ads. Because these are optional, you are under no obligation to purchase.

Automate updates for streamlined computing

The world of apps is a fast-moving one, and things don't stay the same for long. New apps appear on a regular basis and existing apps are constantly updated to improve their performance and also fix any bugs or security issues.

You can manually update apps by visiting your app store and clicking on an *Updates* button or navigating to updates through your account icon. But it's much easier to arrange for all your apps to update automatically.

Windows computer. Open the Microsoft Store and click on your own account icon. Click on the *App settings* option. Drag the *Update apps automatically* button to the on position.

Mac computer. Open the App Store and select App Store > Settings from the menu bar. Check *Automatic Updates*.

iPad and iPhone. Open the Settings app and tap on the App Store option. In the Automatic Downloads section, drag the *Automatically Download New App Updates* button to the on position.

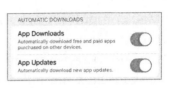

Android device. Open the Google Play Store and tap on your own account icon. Tap on the Settings > Network preferences option, then tap on the *Auto-update apps* option and select how you want the update to be performed.

How to dump no-good apps

Perhaps that news app isn't as interesting as you thought it would be. Or maybe you simply no longer need three versions of sudoku on your phone. Relax. You're not stuck forever with apps you download from the app store. In fact, it's smart to remove them and free up space on your device, both on your Home screen and in terms of the amount of storage they use. And don't worry, if you do remove an app, you can always reinstall it if you change your mind.

Each device has multiple ways to remove apps. Try one of these easy solutions first. Remember, no matter the device, some apps or programs are built into the operating system and cannot be removed.

Windows computer. One way to remove apps or programs in Windows 11 is to open the Start menu, then select Settings > Apps > Apps & features. Click on the app you wish to uninstall and select More > Uninstall.

Mac computer. Click the Finder icon in your Dock, then click on the Applications folder in the sidebar of your Finder window. Find the app you wish to uninstall. If it is in a folder, click on it and look for an Uninstaller. Double-click this and follow the instructions. If your chosen app is not in a folder or doesn't have an Uninstaller, click and hold on the app's icon and drag it to the Trash. It will not be removed from your computer until you empty your Trash.

iPad and iPhone. From the Home screen, press and hold the app's icon you wish to uninstall until a pop-up window appears. Tap on the *Remove App* option, then tap *Delete App* to delete it from your phone.

Android device. Press and hold on an app's icon until an option window opens. Tap on *Uninstall*. Follow any prompts to complete.

It's super easy to reinstall an app that you have removed. For Windows computers and Android devices, simply go to your app store, find the app, and click *Install*.

If you have a Mac, iPad, or iPhone, locate the app in the Apple App Store and click on this icon, which indicates that the app has been downloaded previously.

47 Hobbies

Ever had a hankering to, say, dance the fox trot or cook like Julia Child? Now is the time for all those hobbies you've been putting off.

Like to read? You can download an e-book without ever leaving your easy chair. Or perhaps touring art museums is your thing. Take a room-by-room virtual tour on your laptop. Want to start drawing? Create art digitally without ever needing to buy supplies.

You'll also want to take advantage of all the websites and apps that make learning a new hobby easier than ever. There's really no reason to wait.

Jump-start your hobby online

Searching for a hobby but don't know where to begin? Let these three websites lend a hand.

- Tap into *discoverahobby.com* for a long list of possibilities.

- Whatever you come up with — be it banjo building, knitting, or screenplay writing — *YouTube.com* is a terrific resource for honing your skills and learning from others.

- *MeetUp.com* is a great way to find folks in your area with similar interests. The site makes it easy to socialize while enjoying activities like hiking or testing trivia skills. Check out its free companion app.

Straight talk: Now's the time to learn a new language

It's never too late to pursue a different language, and the digital world makes it easy to get started.

You can find free and affordable online programs at sites like *rosetta stone.com*, *duolingo.com*, and *babbel.com*. Or check out the Foreign Service Institute's free course offerings — complete with full textbooks and audio lectures — at *livelingua.com/fsi*.

Don't have time to learn at your computer screen? Then free language podcasts like those found at *coffeebreaklanguages.com* are available for your listening and learning pleasure.

You can grow a greener garden

The internet provides all the information you need to grow a vibrant and colorful garden. Check out these options that will help your skills, well, blossom.

Websites. Gardening websites have grown as quick as weeds in the spring, but they're a heck of a lot more useful. They provide info on everything from planting basics to pest control and mulching. A few sites to get you started include *gardeningknow how.com*, *gardenguides.com*, and *tastefulgarden.com*.

Instructional videos. These are especially helpful to budding gardeners because they provide visual tutorials on the steps to complete tasks like pruning tomato plants or building raised garden beds. YouTube channels are a great starting point. Just go to *youtube.com* and type the information you're looking for into the search bar.

Apps. Using this type of software on your mobile device can help you identify flowers and plants. Snap a photo and wait for the app to go to work. Free options include PlantSnap, INaturalist, and PlantNet.

Or remove the guesswork when laying out your garden by downloading apps like Plan-A-Garden and IScape. They let you add virtual design elements to your garden so you can visualize how it will look afterwards.

Google remains the top search engine on the internet. And with good reason — it's a remarkably powerful tool. Remember these few tricks when using Google to quickly find what you're looking for.

- Look at Google's categories. They're displayed at the top of the results page and include the words All, Shopping, News, Images, Videos, and More. Select one to define the kind of search you want to do.

- Add a minus sign or hyphen to eliminate results containing certain words. For instance, if you want to search for the tech company Apple Inc. but don't want information on the fruit, enter *Apple -fruit*.

- Use quotation marks if you're looking for very specific information. Searching within quotes will bring targeted results that feature only those words in that specific order. It's a way to exclude irrelevant material.

Turn your attic treasure into cash

Collecting — whether it's stamps, fine china, or baseball cards — is a fun pastime enjoyed by people of all ages. But don't kid yourself. This hobby can also turn a profit. After all, collectibles often increase in value.

And the best way to sell your items for top dollar is to make them available on eBay. That's the online shopping site known for its auctions and consumer-to-consumer sales. So why not make some money with your computer?

First, go to *ebay.com* or its companion app to learn what it's all about. When you're ready to start selling, the website will recommend search terms that buyers often use. Be sure to add them to the name and category of the product you're listing. And you'll want to write a good description with details about what you're offering. Price the item right, and snap photos of it before posting.

Surprise — if you're into arts and crafts, your fun hobby can actually make you money. All you have to do is sell your items on *etsy.com*. The website does most of the heavy lifting, making it easy to set up your online shop, payment system, shipping options, and product listings.

The company has built its platform on unique and one-of-a-kind handmade items. So stick with arts and crafts like candle and soap making, quilting, and woodworking. Before you set prices, see what others on Etsy charge for similar goods. Keep the cost of your items in that range.

Legacy link: Trace your ancestors with 4 top websites

Thanks to the internet, learning about your ancestors has never been simpler. You can now access millions of digital archives on genealogy websites, many of which have corresponding apps. Basic searches on most of these sites are free, but more in-depth access often requires a fee. You'll want to take advantage of what these sites have to offer.

- *Ancestry.com.* The world's largest genealogy site, this resource has historical records from 80 countries. Through DNA testing, it can also help you locate family members.

- *Familysearch.org.* Using this website's records, you can build a family tree, connect with relatives, and share and confirm information with them.

- *Myheritage.com.* In addition to tracing your heritage, this site offers DNA testing to help you track down distant relatives.

- *Usa.gov/genealogy*. This U.S. government website provides free records — including gravesite locaters, military paperwork, census data, and immigrant data — for researching your ancestors. You might also want to check out the National Archives at *archives.gov*.

Home on the fritz? Log on for a fix

No self-respecting do-it-yourselfer would start a project without the proper tools and materials. And in today's tech savvy world, that includes a smartphone and free apps.

For small-scale home repairs, WikiHow offers tons of how-to guides, some accompanied by videos you can view on your smartphone right at the job site.

And the YouTube app is a fantastic option for projects both big and small. Looking to redesign or remodel your home? You'll find lots of inspiration on the Houzz and Homestyler apps.

Fetch lower prices for pet supplies

You can find everything for your pet at great discounts when you know where to look. Instead of buying from a veterinarian, try these sources of affordable pet supplies.

- Visit *chewy.com* and *petco.com* for discounted products. But don't stop there. Sniff around at other online stores, too, like *petsmart.com*, *upco.com*, and *kvsupply.com* — just for starters. Compare costs and factor in whether you'll have to pay shipping and handling.

- Check out warehouse clubs, like Sam's Club and Costco. These usually charge a membership fee, so figure your potential savings before you join. Don't be surprised if you still save money — even with the membership fee. Their online stores — *samsclub.com* and *costco.com* — offer shipping.

Chapter 48 — Food

You're supposed to eat three square meals a day to provide your body with the nutrients it needs. In the past, that meant spending a lot of time buying food and preparing it. Not to mention the cleanup afterwards.

But not anymore. Ordering food online — whether it's from a supermarket, restaurant, or meal kit company — has never been easier. It takes just a few swipes and clicks to get what you're hungering for. How much more convenient could it be? Read on to learn the options, as well as the savings, that are out there.

No scissors needed for big price cuts

Clipping, sorting, and redeeming paper coupons takes time and energy. But you can avoid the hassle — and still save a ton of money — by switching to digital.

So how do you start? Download your supermarket's app or go to the store's website. Log in or sign up for a new account by entering the appropriate information. This step links the electronic coupons you choose to your shopper loyalty card.

Next comes the fun part. Start saving by clicking or tapping on all the coupons you want — from applesauce and coffee to granola and seltzer. The coupons stay in your account until you purchase the corresponding item. Just remember that they carry an expiration date like their paper cousins.

Once you're at the supermarket, shop for your items and head to the checkout lane. But instead of sifting through piles of paper coupons at the register, scan your loyalty card or provide your alternate ID to receive your digital savings. Be sure to check your receipt to ensure that the store redeemed all your coupons.

Prefer shopping for groceries online? Lots of stores allow you to add electronic coupons to your virtual cart. You'll often find deals, for example, on a supermarket's homepage. Other times the discounts show up right next to a specific item.

Online grocery shopping: Save time and money

The traffic ... the crowds ... the hassle. Are you tired of that weekly trip to the grocery store? Thankfully, you can consign it to history. Simply buy your groceries online instead.

The perks are both economical and convenient. For starters, shopping this way makes it easier to stick to a budget. That's because the prices of the items in your virtual cart are added in real time, giving you a running tally of your bill.

And you won't have to traipse up and down the aisles. Just type in the name of the item you want and the available brands and prices will appear on your screen. Select one, click, and move on. You can also browse items by their category.

Still not convinced? Discover what else online grocery shopping brings to the table.

A wide range of products. The number and type of available items have expanded considerably over the years. Now you can often find more variety and cheaper prices when you electronically shop for certain foods like nuts, spices, and beans.

Recurring lists. Most grocery sites keep a record of your purchases. That means you don't have to continually search for staples you buy regularly. You can reorder these items individually or select your entire list.

Delivery options. Receiving your groceries has never been easier or more customized — you can even select the delivery day and time slot. A standard fee usually applies, but can vary from just $3 to more than $10. If you happen to be near the store, choose to pick up your groceries in the parking lot and save on the delivery fees.

Membership offers. These promotions, which vary among companies, provide discounts and reduced delivery costs. Instacart, for instance, charges $99 a year for unlimited free delivery on every order over $35. When you divide that cost over 12 months, it looks more like a bargain, averaging less than $2 a week.

Free trial offers. You'll definitely want to take advantage of these promotions. They often include free delivery for two to four weeks. Make sure you check the terms. Some automatically renew if you don't cancel the service before the promotion ends.

App options. Major online grocery stores have companion apps for their websites. Downloading this software to your smartphone or tablet allows you to place an order even when you're not at home.

If you think you'd like to shop for groceries online, consider the following retailers.

- *walmart.com*, the largest grocery store in the country

- *instacart.com*, which delivers groceries from many companies

- *thrivemarket.com*, a seller of organic products

- *costco.com*, which markets many food products in bulk

You'll also want to check out *target.com* and *amazon.com*.

What's cooking? Let kitchen tech make life easier

Figuring out what to cook for dinner can be a real pain. But it doesn't have to be. The digital world is there to help you create delicious, easy-to-cook meals sure to satisfy even the pickiest of eaters. Here's how to get started.

Online recipes. It happens to the best home cooks — a face-off between that near-empty fridge and a rumbling belly. No need to despair. Just go to *supercook.com* or download the companion app from your device's authorized app store to your phone or tablet. Click on the foods you have in your fridge and pantry, and the software will generate recipes in mere seconds.

Of course, you might have a hankering for something more adventurous. In the mood to cook up a batch of Japanese pot stickers or Nigerian pepper sauce? Look no further than *seriouseats.com* or *yummly.com* for loads of international recipes.

In addition, websites like *bigoven.com* and *foodnetwork.com*, along with their companion apps, offer thousands of ideas and tips for planning a meal.

Online tutorials. New to cooking? Use your smartphone or tablet to play videos with step-by-step instructions on, say, how to make the best scrambled eggs. The great thing about these tutorials is that you can pause them. This allows you to complete a step without feeling rushed or under pressure. You'll discover all you need to get started at sites like *bonappetit.com*, *kitchenstories.com*, and *grokker.com*.

Or you can search the web for a specific dish by typing the words "video" followed by "chicken casserole recipe," for instance. This method provides lots and lots of YouTube channels to choose from.

Got a culinary crisis? The following apps may help.

- Ever find out you're missing an ingredient right in the middle of cooking? If that happens, download the Substitutions app for ideas on what to use instead.

- Converting grams to ounces and cups to liters is enough to give anyone a headache. Same goes for trying to convert an ingredient's volume to weight. Try the Kitchen Dial app for the former and the Cupful or Cook app for the latter.

Flaked salmon in citrus butter sauce with a tasty side of roasted green beans. Sound like a treat you'd find only at a fancy restaurant? Not anymore.

Welcome to the world of meal kits — pre-measured and often pre-prepped, boxed ingredients that come with cooking instructions. It's a fast-growing, multibillion-dollar industry that has taken online retailers by storm. You can order these kits on sites like *blueapron.com*, *homechef.com*, and *everyplate.com*. And don't forget about downloading their companion apps from your linked app store.

But are meal kits a good idea? They can be. Prepared entrees are convenient alternatives for busy people who don't want to rely on fast food. Just know that you'll be paying for packaging, along with the convenience of someone else doing the advance work for you.

Dinner delivered: How to stretch your dine-in dollars

You've settled in to binge watch your favorite TV series when you feel the refrigerator calling your name. Why not order dinner through one of those food delivery apps instead?

Not so fast. All that convenience can come with a hefty price tag. According to *The New York Times*, getting your food this way can cost up to 91% more than if you bought the same meal directly from the restaurant.

That's because most of the popular apps require a delivery fee, sales tax, plus a service fee. If you want just a sandwich, you might even be hit with a "small order" charge. And don't forget that the delivery person should receive a tip equal to 20% of the entire bill, or $3 to $5, whichever is higher.

Of course, it would be less expensive to pick up your menu selections yourself. But if that's not an option, you can still cut the cost of staying home and satisfying your appetite. Here's how.

Go directly to the source. If you're hungry for a deal, shop around for restaurants in your area that offer free delivery. Many also sell gift cards that come with perks, which can offset taxes and service fees. Panera Bread, for example, provides a free $10 bonus card with every $50 purchased in gift cards.

Watch for discounts. Check the websites of food delivery platforms like DoorDash, Postmates, and Grubhub for promotional codes and special offers. Some deals are available to new users, while others apply to everyone. Promos can include free delivery and fixed discounts for certain purchase amounts.

Sign up for a subscription. Maybe you should subscribe to a food delivery service if you find yourself ordering in a lot. For $9.99 per month, for example, Uber One gives you access to free deliveries plus up to 10% off on orders that costs more than $15.

49 Frugal shopping

The quickest way to blow your budget is to shop for anything without a plan. But if your strategy depends solely on old-school newspaper coupons, you're overlooking steep savings. Sure, skyrocketing prices make it tricky to keep costs down on, well, everything. But digital tools help you shop smart and find secret deals — so you can save a boatload on groceries, clothes, cars, gifts, electronics, and more.

Whether you're a savings whiz or in the market for clever new ways to tighten your budget, the online world can help you find the best deals and strategies for holding on to your hard-earned cash.

3 ways to drive down the cost of your dream car

If the thought of spending hours trapped in a car dealership fills you with dread, don't despair. You have other options.

Buy online to avoid haggling. Did you know you can buy a car out of a vending machine? At *carvana.com* you can choose your next ride online by looking through pictures, reading the car's history report, and arranging for financing. Have it shipped to you — often for a fee — or pick it up at the nearest car vending machine. Best yet, you never have to talk with a salesperson.

Other sites are in on this action, too. *Vroom.com* and *nowcar.com* offer virtual car shopping and buying experiences.

Let's make a deal — with help from the pros. Striking a deal is hard work, but for a fee, businesses like CarBargains call around and get competing quotes for you. It could just help you save a fortune on a new car.

Or do the grunt work yourself before you get to the dealership. With resources like the "Accelerate my Deal" tool at *autotrader.com*, you can submit an offer, apply for financing, and schedule a test drive from your computer.

Be prepared when you negotiate it yourself. Going it alone? Get your facts straight before you visit the dealership. Know the fair value of the car and any trade-in you have. Research dealer incentives and expect fees and taxes. Be ready to walk out at any moment if you're not satisfied.

Dealers have an internet department, so try negotiating with them before going to the dealership in person. Or skip the dealership entirely and negotiate with other car owners. You can find used cars for sale online at *ebay.com*, *craigslist.org*, and *facebook.com/marketplace*.

Did someone say free samples? There's no limit to how many you can receive. Just go to *freeflys.com* to order all kinds of goodies. You can also sign up for email alerts to notify you when new complimentary items become available.

Surf to the websites *heyitsfree.net*, *freesamples.org*, *freecycle.org*, and *freestufftimes.com* to get freebies and coupons for just about everything.

Deal hunters spend less with discount apps

The online world is a great place to find a range of stellar bargains — if you know where to look. Discover the latest offers on these websites. They all have mobile apps that you can download through the Apple App Store or Google Play Store, so you can save no matter where you are.

- CouponCabin (*couponcabin.com*) offers online promo codes, printable coupons, and cash-back opportunities.

- Coupons.com (*coupons.com*) compiles the latest deals, online and printable coupons, and cash-back offers from popular stores.

- DealNews (*dealnews.com*) is great for comparison shopping, and claims that every deal they list is the lowest price they could find from a reputable store.

- Flipp (*flipp.com*) has weekly ads, deals, and coupons from more than 2,000 of your favorite stores.

- Hip2Save (*hip2save.com*) highlights the latest offers and freebies, plus provides mobile, printable, newspaper, and store coupons.

- Rakuten (*rakuten.com*) gets you cash back at more than 3,500 stores.

- RetailMeNot (*retailmenot.com*) unearths coupons, promo codes, and cash-back offers, saving you big bucks on clothes, food, and more.

- Slickdeals (*slickdeals.net*) lets users share and confirm little-known discounts so that everyone gets a piece of the pie.

- The Coupons App (*thecouponsapp.com*) helps you score coupons, promo codes, and prescription drug discount card savings.

Never pay full price for clothing again

Looking for new ways to save? Large retail chains were hoping you wouldn't find this out, but you'll never have to pay full price again. In fact, you can save as much as 90%, when you know where and how to shop.

Go online to resale websites. At the top of the list are sites like thredUP and United Apparel Liquidators. They make brand-name clothes available at bargain-basement prices, all without you having to leave the comfort of your home.

Cash in on local consignments. If you like the in-store experience or want to try things on, your neighborhood thrift stores and consignment shops are hot spots. There you can find great quality, as well as low, low prices.

As an added bonus, shopping secondhand reduces the need for new clothing production and saves items that still have life in them from the landfill. This helps reduce fashion waste and protects the environment.

Think outside the box. Bear in mind that the store's layout shouldn't define your trip. Clothing doesn't have a gender, so when browsing keep your eyes open to all available items. If you see a cool sweater in a section you don't usually shop in, don't be afraid to snap it up.

What you shouldn't ignore is the clothing label. This will help you determine the quality of the fabric and whether it needs any special care when laundering.

Stick to a budget. Don't let yourself get carried away by the sweet deals, though. You can rack up a big bill even shopping discounted clothing. So before you start looking, make a list of what you want or need. Then set a spending limit and stick to it. This will help you save money and keep your house clutter-free.

Did you know Amazon has a couple of not-so-known spots that can save you money on tons of items? Just go to *amazon.com/coupons* to find a heap of savings on purchases as diverse as food, pet supplies, pillows, and garden tools. Virtually clip each coupon and add your selection to your cart. The company will apply the discount at checkout.

You can also get great deals on Amazon's used, pre-owned, or open-box products. If you're on your home computer, find the Amazon Warehouse link near the very bottom of the retailer's home page. If you've got the app, type "Amazon Warehouse" in the search box. Begin shopping once the page loads.

If you're tired of being told "your call is important to us" and then waiting forever to get a human being on the phone, you'll be glad to know you don't have to continue wasting your time. That's right — it's now possible to get the human touch with almost every customer service call.

All you have to do is go to *gethuman.com* and enter the name of the company you want to contact. GetHuman will provide the customer service number along with directions on how to speak to a real person in the fastest way. After all, nobody wants to wait on hold.

8 more super sites for seniors

No need to climb every mountain in search of fabulous websites to save money when shopping. Make it a priority to visit these or download their companion apps.

- Check out *acorns.com* for straightforward investing. Each time you buy something with an Acorns-linked card, the company rounds up the price to the nearest dollar and invests the difference.

- Looking for discounted tickets to the theater, concerts, operas, and sporting events? For that and much more, visit *goldstar.com*.

- Go to *groupon.com* for discounts and limited offers on a wide range of products and services. Groupon also offers cash-back deals.

- The site *swagbucks.com* offers members gift cards and other perks for completing online activities like taking surveys and watching videos.

- Online banking service provider *chime.com* markets a debit card that rounds up purchases to the nearest dollar. Chime then transfers the difference to your savings account.

- Visit *SeniorCitizenDiscountlist.org* to uncover senior discounts at grocery stores, restaurants, theaters, and more.

- Rocket Money, at *rocketmoney.com*, aims to help you save on your monthly bills by negotiating better prices and limiting unwanted fees.

- Ibotta partners with retailers and offers cash-back promotions when you shop at participating merchants. Go to *home.ibotta.com* to set up an account.

Tried-and-true tactics: Get tech for a steal

The last thing you want to do is pay top dollar for electronic gadgets. So here are two super reasons to buy new tech at the end of the year.

Get great bargains with Black Friday sales. Lots of people wait until the day after Thanksgiving to go shopping for computers, laptops, TVs, and other electronics. If you're one of them, prepare yourself before the big day by checking the ads on store websites and perusing *consumerreports.org* for their best deal recommendations.

But if you're not one to fight through crowds, don't worry. Most retailers offer Black Friday discounts online. And the following Monday — which is often called Cyber Monday — gives you another opportunity to bargain hunt from the comfort of your computer.

Look to the past to protect your wallet. Many manufacturers release new versions of their electronics towards the end of the calendar year. These updated gadgets come out with cutting-edge bells and whistles — and a hefty price tag.

You'll get the most bang for your buck if you buy the previous version of a product right after the latest one comes out. Last year's model will be almost as good, but a lot cheaper.

Many companies post information about their product release dates on their websites. So check out an item you're interested in throughout the year, in case they introduce a new product at different times.

Buy refurbished and save hundreds

Your first instinct may be to pick up that brand-spanking new computer. But do this instead and you could save a bundle. Three words — buy refurbished devices. These pre-owned electronics are restored, repaired, and tested before being sold at a discounted price.

Many of the major tech companies have options for buying refurbished on their websites. Just search for "refurbished" or "trade in." Check out these options, too.

- EBay has a whole section dedicated to refurbished items. Select the *eBay Refurbished* button on the top toolbar at *ebay.com* to dive in.

- TigerDirect offers a range of tech equipment, some at discounts and some refurbished. Enter "refurbished" into the search box at *tigerdirect.com* and start browsing.

- Newegg sells new and refurbished. Type "refurbished" into the search box at the top of *newegg.com* to find what you're looking for.

Check out each company's policy on refurbished items before you buy. Some brands don't do much more than repackage old electronics, while others put their products through rigorous tests.

Need a filing cabinet? Maybe you're in the market for a bicycle. If so, online government surplus auctions may catch your eye. These websites sell everything from furniture and electronics to vehicles and building supplies. If you're a savvy shopper, you may be able to score a killer deal by browsing through the merchandise at *govdeals.com* and *gsaauctions.gov*.

50 Travel

Your cellphone is likely a must-have traveling companion. Of course you use it to stay in touch as you knock about. And it certainly comes in handy for confirming reservations, calling a cab, or checking your email. But why not take full advantage of its features while vacationing and use its camera to snap a picture of your rental car, your hotel, a trail map, or anything else that will make it easier to navigate a strange place.

In fact, the entire world of technology is designed to give you information, keep you safe, and save you money — even when traveling.

Whether you're on a computer before you go or your mobile device while you're on the go, tap into special websites and apps. They can help you plan your next adventure and turn it into the getaway of a lifetime.

Let handy apps organize your vacation

Both the Apple App Store and the Google Play Store have a Travel category, where you'll find apps that will help out for almost every aspect of your vacation.

Planning. Being organized on vacation can make all the difference, particularly if you have limited time available. Apps for planning your itinerary are therefore an excellent option. In addition to mapping out a timetable, they can offer other types of assistance.

- research destinations
- track travel expenses

- find recommended experiences
- suggest driving routes

Packing. Use these apps to create packing lists so you can check off items as they are safely stowed in your suitcase. Better still, you can keep lists for specific locations — like going to visit the grand-kids — or activities — like skiing or camping.

Look for an app that asks who is going, how long you'll be travel-ing, and activities you'll engage in. This automatically generates a packing template to start you off. Customize it and then duplicate for future trips so you'll have a jump-start on packing for every vacation. Most good packing apps have a free version, but you can pay to upgrade and unlock extra features.

City guides. Every self-respecting city around the world has its own app for guiding visitors to venues, restaurants, and accommo-dations. They often also include sights to see, tours, local customs, and advice on getting around. Some help you book a local guide and work out an itinerary together, while others have you meet up with completely free volunteer guides.

On your phone or tablet, type the city name into your app store's Search bar to see your options. Or go straight to an app from one of the larger players in this industry, like Fodor's, Gogobot, Foursquare, and Pocket.

Seniors travel cheap with a little online help

Vacation should mean rest, relaxation, and no stress. That's hard to accomplish if you spend the entire time fretting over the money it took to get you there.

Make your escape a little more budget-friendly by using the internet to find the very lowest rates on airfares, car rentals, accommoda-tions, and entertainment.

- *cheapcaribbean.com*
- *goibibo.com*
- *orbitz.com*
- *skyscanner.com*
- *travelzoo.com*

- *expedia.com*
- *kayak.com*
- *priceline.com*
- *travelocity.com*

Have map will travel: How not to get lost

No more bulky paper maps that are hard to see and never fold up properly. A map app on your smartphone means you'll always have a comprehensive picture of where you are and where you want to go. Become familiar with some of the functions that can be performed by a map app.

- Get directions. Find your way to almost anywhere from your current location by entering the destination into the app. It will then display the route, which is updated as you travel.

- See nearby facilities. Map apps can show a range of venues in relation to your current location. Search by keyword, such as "restaurants," to display matching businesses in the area.

- Learn local information. If you look up cities or well-known sights, the map app will display general information about it, usually with a link to a website such as Wikipedia for reading more.

- Find transit details. Map apps have a transit function, so you can view options for your current location, like bus or subway schedules. Plus it will display issues or delays with a specific mode of transport.

Note, if you are using a map app, you must have location services turned on. This will let the app determine your current location and then display the appropriate information. Go to your device's

Settings and enter "location services" into the Search box if it is not immediately obvious.

Although you have choices of map apps to download from the Apple App Store or the Google Play Store, two of the best options are already on iPhones and Android smartphones.

Apple Maps. This is the default Apple maps app and is included with all Apple devices.

Google Maps. This excellent, widely used map app includes street view options so you can look around places as if you where actually there. Google Maps can be used on other devices, not just Android.

Hooking in to public Wi-Fi while on vacation lets you access web services and keep in touch with folks back home. To locate hotspot access near your current location, use a Wi-Fi finder app. Three to look at are SpeedSpot Wi-Fi Finder, Instabridge, and WiFi Map. Just remember to always take security precautions when using public Wi-Fi and never log in to any personal accounts or do any online shopping.

Suite dreams: 8 tricks to slash your hotel bill

Don't let a tight budget keep you from enjoying your next vacation. Affordable hotel rooms are actually pretty easy to find. So easy, you'd be crazy to ever pay full price. Heed these eight super smart tips and in some instances, you can get discounts of up to 65%. You'll have money left over for that souvenir T-shirt.

- Off-season, off-peak, shoulder. Whatever you call it, call it cheap. Traveling during "unpopular" times can mean huge savings on lodging. Imagine New England in the spring — no leaf-peepers. Ski slopes in the summer — a mecca for hikers. The southeast in the fall — great festivals. Yellowstone in the winter — stunning scenery.

- Bundle your hotel with your flight or car rental for a stellar package deal.

- You'll never get it if you don't ask, so ask — about discounts for seniors, veterans, groups, associations, employees, memberships, and anything else you can think of.

- Time your booking just right. For best rates, pull the trigger on a hotel for your summer vacation within a month of your trip, says TripAdvisor, the travel planning and booking website. You may snag a great price further out, and that's OK, as long as you can cancel the reservation for a full refund and no penalty if a better deal comes along.

- Join a hotel's loyalty or rewards program, as long as it's free. You could receive discounted rates, points for each stay, and money-saving perks. Look for programs with plenty of locations to choose from and rewards that don't expire.

- The art of haggling is alive and well, and is a skill you need to develop if you want to save some serious travel money. The simplest method? Call the hotel directly, talk to the manager, and ask for a better price, a price match, or an upgrade. Know what competitors are charging and, for best results, try to be flexible on your dates or amenities.

- Scrutinize the fine print before you book and challenge any sneaky fees. You may have to call the hotel for clarification or to opt out of certain services.

- And, of course, you have to comparison shop online or with apps like Hotels.com, Priceline, HotelTonight, Booking.com, Hotwire, HotelsCombined, trivago, and yapta. Roomer Travel, at *roomertravel.com*, is a site that lets you purchase hotel rooms from other people who bought nonrefundable rooms. It's a win-win.

Top 10 Tips for Daily Living

1. Arrange for all your apps to update automatically and you'll always have the latest improvements.

2. Remove unwanted or unused apps from your devices to free up storage space. You can always reinstall them if you change your mind.

3. Discover a new hobby, learn a language, get gardening advice, watch home DIY videos, and more — all through safe and helpful websites or apps you can download to your smartphone or tablet.

4. Make money by selling your attic treasures on eBay, with its large community of collectors.

5. You can avoid the hassle of clipping, sorting, and carrying paper coupons — and still save a ton of money — by switching to digital.

6. Find your favorite recipes online and recreate them with step-by-step video tutorials.

7. Check the websites of food delivery platforms like DoorDash, Postmates, and Grubhub for promotional codes and special offers.

8. When new tech gadgets are released, look to buy the previous model for a quality product at a reduced price.

9. If you shop on Amazon, go to amazon.com/coupons to find a ton of savings.

10. Apps make travel easier and cheaper by helping you find hotel and airline deals, providing customized packing lists, and furnishing interactive maps so you never get lost.

Index

Stage Manager 28
System Settings 31
widgets 34-36
Malware 183-184
McAfee 7
Medicaid 258
Medicare 258
Medication reminders 278
Messenger. *See* Texting; Video chatting
Meta 212
Microsoft Edge browser 189
Microsoft Excel 246
Microsoft MSN Game Zone 292
Microsoft Store 25, 333
Movies and TV. *See also* Streaming
  Amazon Prime Video 309
  Apple TV+ 309
  Disney + 309
  Hulu 309
  Netflix 309
Mozilla Firefox browser 189
Music. *See also* Streaming
  Apple Music 319
  Amazon Music Unlimited 319
  data usage 318
  Deezer 319
  free music 317-318
  Pandora 317
  smart speakers 241-242, 320-321
  SoundCloud 317
  Spotify 318, 320
  streaming options 316-317
  subscription services 319-320
  Tidal 319
  Tidal Free 318
  YouTube Music 318

N

National Do Not Call list 170
Netflix 309
Nintendo Switch 287
Norton 7

O

Old devices, disposing of 129
OneDrive 196-197
Online banking
  safety 145-147
  scams 170

setting up 144-145
Onyx 303
Operating System (OS) 3

P

Pandora 317
Passwords
  creating 150-151
  managers 151, 153-154
  remembering 152-153
  scams 155-156
  security 156
Patient portals 256-257
PayPal 180
Personal alarms 281-282
Personal alert systems
  fall detection 272-273
  features 270-271
  health information 274
  sensors 272
Pets 243, 343
Phishing scams 168-169
Photos
  enhancing 297-298
  organizing 298-299
  printing 299-300
  scanning 301
  sharing 300-301
  taking 295-297
Pinterest. *See also* Social media
  navigating 213-214
  Privacy and data settings 214
Play Store. *See* Google Play Store
Podcasts 321
Portable battery bank 130
Ports 3
Price comparison websites 42, 81, 139
Printers
  inkjet 138
  laser 138
  page setup 139-140
  saving ink 140-141
  wired 139
  wireless 139
Printing
  Mac 119-120
  Windows 119
Privacy online 165
Processor 3

367